LIQUOR
GUNS &
AMMO

Feb 5, 2010 — Randy — Thanks for
Coming over Tonight + Diverting
Elizabeth w/a Couple Games of
Scrabble — "You Can Find Anything
on The Internet" — (I Just Quoted
You, Quoting Her, RE: The Myer's
Lemon)
   It's Always Good To See
You — Hope You Find Something
in Here To Enjoy —————
                Ken

Also by Kent Anderson

Sympathy for the Devil (1987)
Night Dogs (1996)

LIQUOR
GUNS &
AMMO

Kent Anderson

KENT ANDERSON

1 9 98

"Barranca del Cobre" appeared in *Nova Quarterly*,
Dec. 1987; "Call It Neglect of Duty" appeared in
TV Guide, March 12, 1988; "Making War, Not
Love," (originally published as "Soldiers of
Fortune") appeared in *Penthouse*, May 1981;
"Night Maneuvers" (originally published as
"Christian Patriots") appeared in *Penthouse*,
March 1982; "Introduction" to *Trips* by
Charles Fischer, published by Futility
House, 1994. All other material in this
volume appears here for the first time.

FIRST EDITION
Published September 1998

Dustjacket and interior artwork by
Michael Kellner.

ISBN 0-939767-29-5

**Dennis McMillan Publications
11431 East Gunsmith Drive
Tucson, Arizona 85749
http://www.booksellers.com/dmp**

CONTENTS

This book is dedicated to Gary Hanson and Chris Ballmer. Thank you, Gary and Chris. If you hadn't looked out for me, and *almost* never told me to "cool it" back at camp or in Da Nang, when even I knew I was maybe going over the top, I'd still be back there on that black bus, with all the other scared recruits. The driver of the bus never slept, never ate, wearing a wrinkled uniform like ours.

"You did very well, young gentlemen," he said to us. "These poor sorry fuckers they've been sending us lately. . . ?" Life was never the same after the bus. I've written some things I'm proud of. It's all practice. Sitting up front with Death, who drove the Southeast Asian war bus. Sitting up front, joking with Death, who drove with no stops—he was busy. Then one day he looked over at us, smiled, pulled over and opened the door back where we'd got on.

Three new guys got on. He told them, "Put your quarter in *there,* and sit in the back," his goofy bus driver's hat tipped over one eye. We got off and we wished each other luck. Seems like yesterday.

INTRODUCTION

This has been a hard book for me to put together. I wouldn't have done it—I'd have put it the fuck away—if I hadn't promised other people that I *would* do it. I'm a better writer now, and a lot of this stuff looks clumsy and amateurish to me today. I want to throw it away or completely rewrite it or turn it into something else. But if I did that, it would be—not a lie, exactly, but not the truth. I vaguely remember the people I was when I wrote these pieces, like army buddies or cops I've lost touch with over the years. Sometimes I wonder where they are, what became of them. Maybe they're dead or in prison or in the lockdown ward of some mental hospital or rich and unhappy in L.A. But they're gone forever from my life.

Last night I got stalled on something, seized up like an engine running hot, low on oil, rewriting, tightening the prose, trying to pump *rhythm* into the sentences. I told Dennis, "This stuff is awful. In the Introduction let's say, 'Most of this stuff is awful, clumsy shit, but, if there are ever any *serious* Anderson scholars in the future—not bloody likely—they may find this of some interest. Maybe a platoon of "teach-peace" academics can live on my terror-stalked little B-movie life and spend the next forty years chuckling over things they heard, somewhere, I might *well* have done—'" No. Let me die in obscurity. In a freezing rain. At midnight & eaten by *honest* scavengers.

This morning it doesn't look so bad. Some of it gets me to thinking about the world and who I am. Some of it even makes me laugh. It's like riding the bus into the past.

It's good to ride the bus once in a while. I forget about the people who have to ride the bus at night. When I start thinking I'm hot shit, or when I *forget* I'm just white trash who got tough & lucky, it's good to ride the Greyhound with all those losers and psychos and dumb, bad luck motherfuckers I *might* have been, because when I get off in a smoggy, hot 7 A.M. in Reno or L.A. or Richmond or some little café/bus stop up in Idaho that hasn't opened yet; when the doors hiss open & I get out with my cardboard box for a suitcase, I can see things better again. I'm just another guy who rides the bus—nothing more, nothing less. Only difference is that I got the words to *write* about it. That's my job.

Tucson, July 1998

Horse Notes
(1997)

May 21, 1997
To M. K.

They name their horses for minerals. Robert is a retired Morrison-Knudsen engineer. I think they've decided to go with "Realgar," which I found after quite a bit of research— Re-AL-gar. From the Arabic "rahj al-ghar" which means "powder of the mine." An orange-red mineral consisting of arsenic sulfide and having a resinous luster. It was formerly used as a pigment and in pyrotechnics was known as "white fire." I think "Realgar" won out over "Spinel." I trotted Realgar's mother, Pico, bareback in the ring yesterday and Realgar trotted alongside. Pat, the ferrier, down there putting shoes on Dove, was telling me all the ways horses are widely and methodically abused in order to "break," or "train" them, or get them ready to win. It's not like Pat or Robert are touchy-feely New Age horse trainers. I've learned to see it now—how badly, stupidly, viciously, carelessly, and irresponsibly *most* horses are treated. "Pain rising from the earth." A couple days ago I passed a horse alone (they're *herd* animals—they get lonely in a half-acre pen) trying to find some shade under a spindly locust tree. I started weeping. He belongs to someone else, their property, and I can't do anything about it. All I can do is try to be a decent human being day by day, do what I

3

can to make this savage, blundering world a little less awful, not let myself be overwhelmed by everything I can't change —don't go crazy or kill myself out of shame and hopelessness —like a medic with too many wounded in triage—save those who can be saved, as many as I can, and accept the deaths of the others. I haven't written this down before. It's at the heart of the next book, I hope, and my next life.

June 12, 1997
To M. K.

Thanks for the kind words about little Realgar. I try to take photos every week or two up there, but it makes the horses nervous. As if I'm stalking them with the camera. . . .

Went riding yesterday with a friend of Arlene's, E., who has three Arabs. Third or fourth time I've ridden with her. A nice woman who's been riding all her life. Arlene had told me, but I'd forgotten, that she is due in soon for surgery for something they'd found that might be malignant. I thanked her for the ride and said we'd have to do it again in a week or two, and came home. Arlene calls me to tell me that her surgery is noon the next day. (Today). Arlene says to have "positive thoughts" about noon tomorrow. I think I have to pray and my first thought is to talk it over with Praying Mantis. But I want something else working for that night. So I think, "Realgar." I call her house, but no one's home. On their machine I tell her thanks again for the ride today, and "Hey, I'm going up in the hills to see the horses. I'll give your regards to Realgar, ten weeks old now. He's done magic for me. Talk to you soon."

If I talk to Realgar about it, maybe *he'll* do the magic so E. will be OK. It's almost 9 P.M., and raining. But I have made this deal and if I don't find Realgar and things turn out bad at noon, well. . . . For two hours I walk the hills in the rain and *dark* looking for seven horses and a foal over 150 acres, on the treeless hills they run on. A little worried now about lightning strikes up there, clothes heavy with rain, stopping to get my bearings in the lightning flashes so I don't step off into a ravine. I walk on, hands in my wet pockets, making noise so I won't spook the horses. "Hey, where are you guys tonight. . . . " To myself, "Just walkin' and talkin' to myself, that's me, uh huh. . . . " Singing a whiny Neil Young song I heard on the radio, "My my heyee, haaay . . . it's better to burn out than to fay-ed awayee . . . " Across the canyon are all these million dollar houses, big screen TVs in huge windows–no curtains because no people are supposed to be over here, just *nature*–all the TVs twitch "blueblue blue. Blue. Blueblueblue. . . . " like death throes, I think.

I swear I walked an acre, but no luck. I'm soaked, cold, muddy after falling in the mud a few times. Then I think, as long as I put the fix in by noon tomorrow, I'm OK. I go back up this morning, find the horses and talk to Realgar. Arlene calls this afternoon and tells me it was benign.

I'm feeling strung out and exhausted. Got a raw butt from riding four hours yesterday and gotta get up at 6 A.M. tomorrow to drive to Mountain Home and spend the day (probably in the rain) helping a former student and couple of ranchers "move cows." I'm not a good rider and I know I'll look stupid, but that's where stories come from.

June 17, 1997
To E.

After midnight again. I spent the evening in a little room boiling alcohol and talking. What a world. Andrea has this, apparently well known, insane white Arab stallion who's 22 or 24 years old. A great character, I'm thinking, for the next book. Robert and Arlene know about him. They called him "Tor," and Arlene says he has thousands of endurance miles on him. The moment I saw him I thought of the actor Claus Kinski in the movie *Aguirre, The Wrath of God.* That's who he looks like. Insane, self-destructive, "self-mutilating," the whites of his eyes showing, dangerously out of control, gorgeous. Obviously I "identify" with him.

I'm baby-sitting the Morris' horses this week, which is a pleasure. Got six copies of a new French edition of *Sympathy* in the mail today. Good looking cover, but I got screwed out of a lot of money, not much left after the publisher, my editor, the foreign agent and my former NY agent got their cut.

My former friend who's doing ten years in a penitentiary in Texas after a shootout with police left him paralyzed from the stomach down from a .357 magnum police slug in the spine—who's been writing me insane, bitter, angry and vicious letters the last 18 months—tells me that I'm "doing" these horses as a kind of watered-down Hemingway thing. Hemingway, he says, went to Africa to face animals who could "tear him apart," whereas the most a horse can do is maybe "nip" me. I wrote him that "the horses are a metaphor for every tragedy in our lives . . . more beautiful, powerful, and noble than we are . . . yet they are our slaves." Pretty romantic idea, but I believe it.

June 18, 1997
To E.

Horses saved you, huh? I'm laughing, because that's what I say (mostly to myself). A year and a half ago I was drunk for five months, in an affair with a 23 year old girl, a .12 gauge shotgun round always in my pocket after Judith hid the hand-guns.

I was up to feed the horses tonight and it was beautiful up there, black sky moving toward Tablerock, lightning strikes, a huge section of rainbow rising into the rain. I find the horses way back in the hills. I yell to them, "Come on . . . I got grain down here, comeon. . . . " I walk closer, squat down, arms around my knees, and study them. They don't move. Stand up. "Comeon, I got grain. . . . " moving my hands like flippers, "comeon. . . . " Champagne starts down. She's kind and thoughtful—wise. I take my shirt off up there because it's hot, and the breeze coming from those black clouds—the air feels like a miracle across my chest and arms and shoulders and face. "OK, girl, come on, I got grain down here." The others turn and follow her, trotting, then cantering as I turn my back to them, listening to their hooves in the rain closing the distance, then *huge shoulders* slam past me on both sides, the herd breaking around me and down the hill, little Realgar, ten weeks old, dancing leaping, floating around and through them like a manifestation of the best thought I've ever had in my life.

7

June 21, 1997
To E.

Woke up with a virus or food poisoning or a bad combination of legal and illegal drugs. For two or three hours there, I
thought my heart or part of my brain was gonna blow up and
adios, motherfuckers. I even changed clothes, out of my cutoff
jeans and torn, Realgar-chewed purple T-shirt, so if I ended
up in the emergency room or the morgue I'd look better. A
weird, out-of-it plateau—I ask myself, "Do you give a shit if
you're dead or alive? I would like to write this third book. I
think it's there, and there ain't nobody else who can write it."
A little later, or a little earlier, I thought, "What would you
miss if you were dead?" Anything? . . . the horses. When I go
up there, they tolerate me, a herd wannabe. But they're the
closest thing to a family I've ever had, along with 5 or 6 guys
in the A-camp up in I-corps, but that was a real lunatic, suicide
brotherhood.

I go up there in the dark, dizzy and sick, because those
horses and hills are my salvation if anything is. Storm coming
in, huge golden-bottomed clouds moving north like movie
spaceships. I take off my shirt to feel that wind, sing "Poor
boy blues" so I won't spook the herd. I'm downwind from
them and they don't see me yet. I say hello to all of them, sit
down, play with Realgar, who's after the shirt. Sun's down
now, no more gold clouds, all black&white. Absolutely
peaceful, the sound of horses ripping grass up and chewing
it. Champagne scratching her butt on the skeleton of a
sagebrush burned away last summer. The wind. Then, just
over the hill at the police firing range in the next canyon—it
must be automatic weapons night—they're firing 3 and 5 and
7 round bursts of M-16 or Car 15, or AR 15s, .223 rounds, the

sound as distinctive to me as the rotor pounding of a Huey helicopter or a Cobra gunship or my own footsteps on a dirt road in the dark. It's late dusk, the time of night when ambushes pay off, the window of last delicate light when, if you've got your shit together, you might get to kill some people. While you can still see you get the Claymores out, make eyecontact with your Montagnards, know where everybody is— smelling the air for Vietnamese cigarettes, fish sauce, or some Vietcong who's holding his column up while he takes a shit— "ah, motherfucker . . . come on down. That's the last shit you're ever gonna take 'cause we're gonna kill you real soon. . . . " All pumped up and laughing inside, exchanging a *look* with Rau or Chung or Mr. Minh, hunkering down on your belly so you're not in the backblast of a Claymore when it goes off. It's gonna be a while before they get there, so you take a Coke outta your pack and *quietly* drill a little hole in the top with your K-bar knife, suck the sweet warm Coke out and burn the sugar away, the army-issue amphetamines singing in your blood. You smell grass and dirt and gun oil and your own sweat . . . but . . . it's 1997, not 1969. I'm listening to horses eat. Over my left shoulder the illuminated cross up on Tablerock is just visible. One of those moments and minutes of Grace that I've worked for, I suppose, and earned. When it's all given to me, where myth and fable and fairytales come from. If I can just stay cool, sane and alive, and write this third book. . . .

June 23, 1997
To E.

It's 4:30 Monday afternoon. I'm feeling sort of crazy and have turned off the phones and am hiding out. I keep thinking about that piece I wrote the other night, the part where I say

I'm "pumped up and laughing inside" about getting to ambush someone. I left a part out of it. Being scared. Of course, I'm scared too, but if you hug the fear close enough, it starts to purr and go to sleep in your arms, its ears still alert, still smelling the breeze. Your arms start to ache after a while from holding fear, but you know that you'd damn well better keep hugging it until the shit happens and he bounds away and you're all right and know that he'll come back to you. Unless you're dead and don't need him anymore. Either way, that's fine.

June 30, 1997
To E.

Went up into the hills tonight when it was blowing, pelting, sheets-of-it-on-the-windshield raining. Three layers of shirts for insulation. Judith said I should wear a raincoat and I said "I don't believe in them." (Because if you're really moving around, you'll get wet anyway, but more importantly, if you're moving through the jungle where people are trying to kill each other, the rain "patters" on the raincoat, which makes it easier for the "enemy" to hear you and harder for you to hear them. I can't, or won't, give up those lessons from 25 years ago.) I park by the gate, just as Champagne comes down the hill and goes under the roof of the tack shed. I get out of the car—rain going blam, blam, blam on me—look up for the other horses, then decide to go talk to Champagne 'cause she's been pretty nice to me lately, since I rode her last. But she doesn't want to talk, looks away, rain hammering the tin roof, pouring in torrents off the corners. I bend down to look up into her eye . . . naw, she doesn't want that, starts to walk away, into the rain. I say, "That's OK, girl. You were here first. Stay here, I want to go up there anyway. See you later." I walk up the first of the hills, slipping, catching myself, thinking how many sunflowers there are gonna be this year, make it past the road onto the grass, where I keep walking on thousands of tiny, closed white morning glories—no way I can *not* crush some of them. I walk, come into the black skeleton of a huge (I think) bitterbrush, 7 or 8 feet tall, the circle of soil around its base absolutely black and without any kind of vegetation and I wonder why. Is the soil burned dead, is the pH fucked up, what? But the dead plant dominates this sweep of the hillside, and I say to it, "Hello old grand-father, how are you?" And the rain is slamming down—earlier I'd thought how it's good to go walking in the rain if you're weeping, no one will know. I find the horses, and I hadn't expected to, back in the main bowl, almost to the fence line half a mile into the hills. I whistle, let 'em know I'm coming. Talk to myself. Go around, uphill from them, and squat down. They're sleeping, but alert, and it occurs to me that I slept in the same way back there in the jungle when the rain was so bad, monsoon season, rain, rain, rain, like a bad dream, forget trying to stay dry, forget making any klicks, any movement until it slacks off because you can't *hear* in that weather, the rain and wind wash away any smell of the enemy, so you better just hunker down and wait, wet and shivering, *think* the cold away, go to sleep sitting in a squat, your nose to the wind, your ears, if you can, tilted into the wind so it doesn't roar in them, go to sleep. I was asleep, it counted as sleep, but I smelled and heard everything, tuned in, and I could be up and running in half a second. Just like the horses. I squat up there for half an hour, sleeping with them, remembering that war, but watching them sleeping.

I've never found the horses in rain this heavy and I'm spooking them, even though they know me. They've turned, butts to the wind, on three legs, the right or left rear foot

11

raised, eyes slightly open, ears alert and moving, listening to me, a lunatic human up there in driving rain. Twelve week old Realgar's confused, trying to pick up signals from the herd and do what they do (downhill from me about 20 yards). I'm singing, "I can see clear-ly now, the *rain* has gone . . . I can see all ob-*sti*-cles in my wayee. . . . " and making them uncomfortable like I do people sometimes. "Who is this guy up here in a driving rain, singing, waiting for us to tell him secrets of the universe?" Pyro is always the sweetest and most forgiving to me. Not the smartest boy in the world, or, god knows, the most dominant, but he's almost always brave. He comes up to me when the others want me to go away. Bless his heart. What a fine boy he is. I know it's shamefully anthropo-morphic, but I believe what I'm writing. So fuck a bunch of scientists. If I can keep this up, I will learn something about myself and horses and the Universe. I'm grateful for the chance.

July 6, 1997
To E.

Gotta eat, get some sleep, I'll call mañana—to the point where I'm thinking in Spanish, and I'm awful at it, bad grammar, malapropisms (I once ordered "fisherman" for dinner instead of "fish"). Anyway, I was thinking, "Volver, volver, volver—luz, noche, dolor, clemencia, valentía—dar el camino norte, mi hermano . . . buen suerte."

July 6, 1997
To E.

". . . but give me . . . weeeed, whites and wieee-ine . . . and I'll be willin' . . . to be movin'. . . . " I heard that song on the radio yesterday for the first time in 20 years. Linda Ronstadt's version? "I been waarped by the rain, driven by the snow, drunk and dirty, but don't you know . . . that I'm still . . . (double beat) willin'. . . . "

Last night I hooked up an old turntable and speakers. Today played some "Vietnam" records. Went back to Mai Loc and Minh Long for a while. It was all weirder than I remembered. I, Me, Mr. Honesty, trying to fuzz out how insane and magnificently horrible it was. I was a creature from Jupiter, breathing boiling ammonia fumes instead of air. I *think* I was happy. My eyes would roll back listening to "Back in the USSR," or "As My Guitar Gently Weeps," "Hot Summer Days," "Can't Find My Way Home" by Blind Faith—then, it's time to go— with a handful of Montagnards, or Vietnamese from the Combat Recon Platoon. I didn't much like Vietnamese, but these guys, they were *so mean* that, even though they were Vietnamese, they were OK. Beautiful pieces of pure death-work. I'd see 'em pacing the CRP compound in the heat, stiff-legged, bent at the waist slightly, eyes down, pacing— waiting to be let loose out there. I knew I was dead and I was death. I didn't go out there in the dark at 5 A.M. with five or seven Yards or CRP guys to "stay alive" or "check things out." I went out to kill people. I wasn't ordered. That's what I wanted to do. That was how I defined myself. (*I haven't even thought about this for . . . a long time.* Killing people. Well.)

Probably, love has kept me alive, I'm thinking. Not hate, not meanness, not anger or revenge. Love. I'm a fool just like everybody else, I guess. . . . willin' . . . to be, mooovin' . . .

July 26, 1997
To E.

Got back from Missoula in the middle of the night–drove up yesterday morning for a party Crumley was having. On the way up, via Challis and Salmon, every mile stunningly beautiful, watching horses along the way. They know things humans don't. They're hooked into the magnetic center of the earth. Came back the next day, still drunk–stopped at the Lolo Pass visitor center and read a brass historical marker referring to an incident on July 23, 1877. I was there July 20. 750 Nez Perce and two thousand horses crossing the pass, pursued by US cavalry. I could *hear* those horses as I walked to my car.

I know a guy who lives in Grangeville, and decided that if I could just make it there (" . . . without gettin' killed or caught") I'd call him. Spend the night with him and his wife. No answer at his house, but I was starting to feel better, so I drove on, down a 7% grade out of Grangeville where I see another historical site. I pull over. It's a map of the huge valley below. I look down at the map and then up at the valley itself, where a hundred "militia" attacked an advance party of Nez Perce– 80 of them–right there below where I'm standing. Reading between the lines, it said that a hundred yahoos decided "let's go kill us some fuckin' Indians." The Nez Perce killed "a third" of the yahoos and none of the Nez Perce were killed. According to the marker, and who knows? Like they say, "What is history but fiction agreed upon?" Finally, a Nez Perce chief named Two Moons shouted, "Let them go (the white boys). None of us has been killed." They could have slaughtered more but chose to ride off. The Indians used mostly bows and arrows and only a few rifles and still kicked the white boys' asses. A big reason they did so well was because they had those horses and could ride like . . . like I'll never be able to ride. The hair on the back of my neck is standing up and I'm weeping behind my sunglasses. What must those horses have meant to the Nez Perce that they would drive 2000 of them over the pass while being chased by the calvary? How amazing that I ran into Robert and Arlene and the horses when I did. I'd be lost for sure if I hadn't.

I went down there this morning, hungover and still a little drunk. Today is a free day, I decided, because I drove all night and earned a day where I don't have to type. Watched Realgar for a while. What a piece of work he is, seventeen weeks old. He's gonna take over the herd one day.

September 20, 1997
To E.

Drove down the hill to see the horses, a tape of Roseanne Cash singing, " . . . soon we'll be sleeping in Paris, and you can set those angels free. . . . " and with the song came an image of my life, an almost out of control train rocking on the tracks, everything around me a blur. As long as I don't panic, I'll stay on the tracks, through this focused and lucid tunnel of light. I realized the image is a Turner painting, "Wind, Steam, and Speed."

The horses are all by the roundpen, or in the trees across the cracked-mud creek. Pyro walks out of the trees and across the creek to see me. I have a connection with him that I don't have with the others. He's sweet and ingenuous and reminds me of myself when I was a kid in the 2nd or 3rd grade in Minnesota. I say, "How you doin', Big Pyro? What a boy," stroke his neck, and as I breathe into his nostril I remember Robert Painter working with one of the yearlings. He pursed

15

his lips and breathed into the yearling's nose, the first person I've seen do that other than me. I ask him about it, how sometimes a horse doesn't want me to do that, like I'm assuming too much, acting rude and too familiar with the horse. He nods, tells me "When you do that, your breath should say to the horse, 'everything good in me into you,' and when you inhale the horse's breath, think it's 'everything good in you into me.'"

Since I'm thinking about Painter and the yearlings:

When I first climbed into the 12 x 12 pen (four moveable corral "panels" that connect with hinges and 8 inch steel pins), he told me to "exude confidence." I didn't have it, but obviously what you do is fake it until it becomes real, like, at some point, in *all* of this, you realize, "Hey, I'm not faking it anymore, it's real."

Painter tells me that every touch should be soothing to the horse, and when you look into his eyes, you should think, "I really like you. I really like you." I asked him how does that work. Maybe all it is, is when you *think* that, it's simply manifested in the way you move and touch the horse. The horse doesn't actually pick up on your thoughts. Painter says horses sense things that we can't, implying that they *do* pick up on your thoughts.

Painter says he tries to "get into his (the yearling's) mind," and lets the horse get into *his* mind.

We'd worked three or four of the horses. . . .

(RP trying to teach me to read their eyes, "See it, see the fear in his eyes?" Or anger. "The eye gets hard and shiny. When the ears go back, you know he's angry and is going to do something about it.")

Each yearling took 40 minutes or so before Robert could put his hand on them. The next horse was different, a good colt, smart, initially defiant—one of the qualities I like about

16

the Barbs–I see it in Fleck, too–when they're in danger, when they obviously feel trapped and you're backing them into a corner, they don't panic or get hysterical or mean. Even as their skin quivers and they're poised to bolt, they're *thinking* about it. (When they're thinking something over in a less back-against- the-wall situation, like "Should I let him touch me?" or "Should I submit to him, it looks like I can't get away," they make a chewing motion and lick their lips.) Anyway, after only five, or ten minutes at the most, Painter slips through this new yearling's "space bubble" up to him and puts his hands on him, that quick. I asked him how did he do that so soon. He says, "I saw it in his eyes. He told me, 'You can touch me if you want to,' and I said, 'OK, I will.'" It was obvious *something* had happened. It was a smart yearling, I think, who realized he had no choice, it was inevitable, so why not go ahead and submit. He wasn't just lazy like another, disappointing, colt. "Submit" isn't quite the right word. He trusted Robert. (While working with one of the yearlings, maybe this one, Robert told me the horse told him, 'You said you'd take care of me, so take care of me.')

(Later–I looked at my original notes and saw that what Robert actually said was: "He gave me permission to touch him, so I did." A real difference in attitude.)

I'm in the middle of the roundpen, Fleck circling me, stopping, one rear hoof cocked, relaxed, trying to figure me out. I see it in his eyes. Tourmaline and Nikki are penned up next to the roundpen, under a big locust tree. Tourmaline is being a bitch, as usual, pinning her ears at Fleck, charging the fence next to him, even kicking the roundpen when Fleck is close, but he ignores her. Pyro comes over as Fleck drinks out of the big green bucket against the inside of the roundpen. He works his nose through the slats to breathe into Fleck's nostrils, but Fleck isn't going for it. Realgar dorking around like the kid he is. Pico seems to be ignoring 5 month old Realgar, working on a short patch of grass, but she's watching, paying attention to everything going on. Champagne on the other side of the creek keeping her own council. I sit here in the roundpen, all this activity, relationships and interactions happening around me. I'm aware of it all, paying attention, yet relaxed, at peace. The horses help me meditate, pray. Theory I had last night—"meditation is connecting with yourself, and prayer is connecting yourself with the universe."

October 15, 1997
To Dennis

John Quinn suggested the title, "Final Protective Fires" which I like better. Let me know what you think.

Went riding again this afternoon. Ten miles up in the hills. Rocky ravines and stream beds, steep downhills, goat trails. It keeps me physically scared. Something I seem to need. Like love.

The new title is a military term. You have all your weapons set up so even if it's dark and raining and freezing and you've been awake on the perimeter for days because the enemy has been harassing you, planning to overrun your camp, you can stumble out and crank the traversing mechanism of the .50s so they're blowing those big rounds through the wire at about mid-waist level, drop the 105s straight down like huge shotguns firing flechette canisters. Elevate the mortars to drop their rounds into the perimeter wire, blow the foogas and finally, if you're in the arc of an artillery fan, call in fire on top of you, and it's "Whoop-eee we're all gonna die."

I love the names of those big firebase guns. Numbers—175s, 155s, eight inch—no time for abstractions and metaphors—*numbers*. Big old rounds, you listen to them coming your way.

This morning, just now, 28 years later, I'm back there. They always sound like your friends, even if they're coming to kill you. Hearing them again. Ripping the air–they know who they are, and have no indecision or fear. It's monsoon season –no gunships, no "relief" forces because none of them can get through the weather over the mountains. And even if they did that, they couldn't land or bomb, couldn't see through the cloud cover or fog.

They shake the earth around you, geyser mud, a few seconds later those red, hot, claw-sized pieces of shrapnel hissing into the mud . . . oh, you can smell the sulfur . . . Comp B, I think, unless I'm making this up as I go along from old war movies. You know that line from *Apocalypse Now,* " . . . it smells like victory." That sulfur smells like certainty and courage and "everybody's gotta die someday, my brother."

Went riding for three hours this afternoon with Arlene Morris. Got a sore butt. She scared me shitless going down some of those hills. "Huh? You going down there? Really?" Sure. Of course. Nice ride. Kind of smoothed me out. Finally above this one valley I started remembering about calling air strikes. Are they better during the day–you hear 'em, Phantom jets, way off, then you're talking to the senior pilot–usually there's two planes, one just behind and to the side of the lead ship, you hear 'em, the pilot's voice on your PRC 25 is raspy, saying something like, ". . . uh, this is Ringneck Two Niner . . . that's us you hear, uh. . . " and they *appear*–they're above you then past you, shaking the ground where you're laying, scared of getting killed, your chest hammering, blowing your hat off and then . . . shit, you're happier than most people ever are in their lives. Or . . . at night, "uh, this is Ringneck Two Niner . . . with a friend, har har, coming to deliver that selected ordnance you requested, and. . . . "

Blood & Redemption
(1983)

Easter Sunday

I don't know what I expected. A tinny little Mexican circus. An animal act with costumes. I'd seen parts of *Blood and Sand* on late night TV—Tyrone Power in pancake makeup as the Spanish Matador from Culver City. I'd read Hemingway's phony-tough-guy bullfight prose. I knew the bull gets killed in the end, but I didn't really understand that, because what I'd read and seen had been censored and sanitized for tender American sensibilities. Most Americans do their best to stay in a TV dreamworld of undying love, cartoon violence and happy endings, and even though I'd killed my share of people in Vietnam, worked as a street cop in the ghettos of East Oakland and North Portland, wading through human death and despair five nights a week, doling out *more* than my share of violence and street justice, even *I* wasn't prepared for a bullfight, for the bloody and brutal sacrifice of ~~Siete~~ *Toros Bravos,* "~~Seven~~ Brave Bulls."

The Juarez bullring was small, the size of a traveling one-ring circus in Butte or Barstow, but it was closer, much more immediate than I'd imagined. The first fight had already begun, the bull softened up by the *picadors'* bullet-headed lances, his back covered with blood that had begun to gel in the hot afternoon sun, fresh blood seeping beneath the old, coagulating, growing on his back like a monster parasite. Still standing, my fifty-cent rented cushion under my arm, I decided that I was not going to like the bullfights and almost walked out. I looked back at the bloody bull. He couldn't

21

leave. He would die no matter what I did. And how was this any worse than being run through a chute into a concrete slaughterhouse after a short life in a steaming feed lot?

It got worse. The first fight was botched by the *matador*. He tried four times to kill the bull, driving his downcurved sword only halfway to the hilt each time, missing the heart, the sword flopping, loosening, and falling to the ground as the bull charged past. Four bloody and sad "moments of truth," the bull staggering from loss of blood when the *matador* finally dropped him with his second thrust into the base of his brain, and even then I wasn't sure the bull was dead. Half a dozen drunken American soldiers behind me, skin-headed trainees from Ft. Bliss, took cigarettes from their mouths to shout, "He's no *matador*," and "Give him a machine-gun." I was ashamed we were from the same country and looked back at them the way I'd look back at people talking at the movies, or in church.

The "butcher," a heavyset, middle-aged man wearing a white uniform not unlike a butcher back behind the glass at Safeway, walked over, knelt in the sand, worked a wide, short-bladed knife back & forth into the base of the bull's skull, severing the spinal cord, then leaned away as the bull finally kicked, convulsed and died.

The crowd was on its feet, the men whistling, two fingers in their mouths, an expression of disapproval, I realized—their way of booing.

The soldier-trainees behind me screamed insults in English as the *matador*, in disgrace, walked stiffly across the sand and out of the ring. I wanted to break the soldiers' noses and jaws to shut them up, beat them into a hospital bed, but when I turned to glare, challenging them to shut up or "let's go, motherfuckers," they didn't see me, their eyes stupid and drunk, the kind of third-rate troops they'd sent to walk, smoking cigarettes and joking, into obvious ambushes, step on mines, smoke dope at fire bases and drop artillery on themselves, accidentally shoot each other on guard duty, and lose that war I'd been in.

Two horses in harness were led in, up to the bull, where something spooked them and they bolted away. They were caught, calmed down, hooked up to the bull and led off, leaving a bloody trail in the sand that was quickly raked and shoveled away. The band struck a single note, held it, held it, and began to play, announcing the entrance of the second bull as he charged out of a tunnel, through an open gate–the *puerta de los sustos,* the "gate of fright"–and into the ring. He was a magnificent animal, massive chest and shoulders and neck, skidding to a stop in the center of the ring, a primal force, like a storm or lightning. Wheeling, a gossamer of saliva spooling from his jaws, he charged the *matador's* assistants, *peones,* who had taunted him, sidestepping into the ring, then running–like players trying and failing to steal second base– back behind the bull'seye-painted barricades.

The five o'clock sun in my eyes, I look around the arena– except for me and the soldiers and a handful of others, they are all Mexicans–young couples, families, children and nursing infants, mostly poor, some obscenely rich. A beautiful two year old girl, tiny gold rings in her ears, looks down at her new white Easter dress, spreads her skirt with both hands, utterly happy. A hot, strutting redhead, skin the color of cherrywood, wearing skintight jeans, a white silk blouse and high-heeled boots, takes a cigarette from her coral-red lips and blows smoke from the corner of her mouth, working her way back to her seat.

The bull circles the ring, trotting now, head up, confused, frightened and angry, looking for someone to punish for driving him out here into the sun. A lot like me, I think, then

23

the band sounds and pairs of *picadors* canter in from four directions, wearing low-crowned hats that lower their foreheads, making them look slightly retarded. The crowd whistles and boos them as, I'll discover, they always do. They are the first villains in this morality and death play.

The *picador's* outside leg is covered from hip to ankle in hinged silver armor that weighs thirty pounds. His stirrups are the size and shape of coal scuttles. The lance he carries, I discover through my binoculars, is tipped not with a blade, but a brutal pyramid-shaped iron point. His horse's outside eye, the eye that would see the bull, is blind-folded with rags.

The brave horses, at a touch from their rider's knee or heel, sidestep, turning with the bull. They are draped from withers to tail and down almost to their hooves with quilts that remind me of moving van padding, only thicker. The *picadors* sit their horses straight-backed, with great formality, eyes forward, not on the bull even as they move with him, lances at their sides, waiting—until the bull lowers his head and charges one of them, driving his horns into the horse and up, lifting him to the tips of his hooves. The *picador* leans from his suspended horse, over the bull, and drives his lance down, between the bull's shoulders, puts his weight into it like a man poling a skiff, shouldering it deep into the muscles that power his horns. When all four have worked him over like thugs in a vacant lot, the crowd begins to whistle and boo. *Enough.* The band strikes up, *enough,* and plays the four horse-men out of the ring. The bull is bloody and less defiant, not holding his head as high as before, the toss and hook of his horns not so quick now. The smell of blood, faint and metallic, rises in the heat, mixed with cigarette smoke, with grilled chorizo, carnitas, and fat french fries in paper bags for sale by a pockmarked Indian a few rows down. *"Cerveza, soda, pappas. . . ."*

It had been about the same time of day, late afternoon, and hot. Tall, dry razor grass twitched and crumbled around our bomb crater while we tossed out the hand grenades—they looked like beer can rattles with wooden handles—that bounced and rolled down the lip of the crater, smoking and hissing. Blood that didn't sink into the ground but beaded up, rotating in place like tiny worlds, taking on a skin of red dust. My Montagnard squad leader took a carbine round through his belt buckle and I held his hand while he vomited sardines and noodles, and called for a medivac. A pair of Cobra gunships were already on the way.

After the gunships had finished, we walked out among the NVA bodies, the dead and wounded, some of them waiting to kill us, pretending they were dead. One of them rose up, the grenade in his hand exploding as I shot him again. He took most of the blast and shrapnel, but the concussion slapped me in the chest and forehead and nose, and a shard of cast iron shrapnel blew past my ear so close I felt its heat. I left my body for a little while then and watched myself go through two more eighteen round magazines. I killed a lot of people that day, some wounded and helpless. Nobody, I realized a few years later, surrendered or took prisoners over there.

The music slows, softens, marches in place, until trumpets announce the entrance of the three *banderilleros.* Each of them, in turn, faces the bull, feet together, arms extended like a high diver about to leave the platform. In each hand they hold a *banderilla*—a ribbon-wrapped, two-foot wooden rod with a barbed icepick tip. As if on some signal, bull and *banderillero* charge each other. The *banderillero* sidesteps, driving his fluttering *banderillas* into the bull's bloody neck where they shudder and droop and twitch as the bull skids to a stop, wheels, paws the sand, facing the next *banderillero.*

After the war I spent fall and winter in a cottage in Mendocino, California. I couldn't find a job, even in the lumber mill up in Ft. Bragg. No one would hire a Vietnam veteran because they were *considered to be crazy and dangerous, which, in my case, was true. Most days, I woke up late in the morning with a hangover. I was drinking a gallon of wine a day—Red Mountain wine which cost $4.00 a gallon at Safeway. I'd bought a Colt Python .357 Magnum revolver, and I spent a lot of time in the mornings looking at it. Holding it. Loading and unloading the fat hollowpoint rounds. When I held it up to the light and looked down the barrel, I could see the brass-jacketed slug, waiting for me like a snake in a hole.*

I began to see the pattern in the bullfight, a drama to weigh courage and accept inevitable failure and death. It is not a fight or a sport, but a religious ritual, a three act drama—*Picadors. Banderilleros. Matador.* No one wins or loses. Everyone dies eventually, but in the face of inevitable death, we—men, bulls, and horses—can be heros by standing our ground, charging, taking the blows and cuts, facing and accepting death bravely. The bullfight reminds us, reassures us, that *every* life is hard, filled with failure, ending in certain death, and our job is to face and accept it with courage.

Mas musica announces the fourth bull, and I realize that even the tinny little band, playing against the fireball of the setting sun, reminds us of our mortality and our obligations.

The fourth bull is the best yet, so black that he charges into the ring like a shadow with substance, absorbing energy from the sun, galloping from barricade to barricade after the taunting *peones*.

I watch the *picadors* in the chute, waiting for the music to call them into the ring, wishing each other well, patting their horses. I find myself weeping and wishing *them* well, and the bull, and the *matador*.

That winter after the war, in a leaking cottage heated with a wood stove, I stopped trying to walk into town during the day. The last time I'd tried, I was stopped the moment I walked out the door into the sun. My ears rang and clicked, my eyes shut down to black-bordered tunnel vision, I got dizzy, afraid I'd fall down and lay there helpless. I was afraid, I realized later, that I might kill someone and be sent to prison or locked up in an insane asylum. I didn't think I would ever be able to live among normal, decent people again.

I spent the days alone, down among the tidal pools below the bluffs, watching the tide and the weather and the relentless life and death drama of the sea. I'd crouch there over the tidal pools, careful not to disturb anything, and watch the starfish and abalone, the minnows and anemone stalking each other. By dusk I'd usually feel all right. Everything in the ocean did what it was supposed to do. The tide moved in and out like my own breathing, the sun sank into the gunmetal sea, the moon appeared, and I'd allow myself to hope that there was some logic to life—that I might discover it if I stayed brave and didn't blow my brains out.

The fourth bull, bloody now from the lances, lifts and topples a *picador's* horse on top of the *picador*. He manages to free the leg under the screaming horse, but can barely stand because of the heavy armor on the other leg. The *matador* and his *peones* draw the bull away. Other assistants get the hysterical horse to his feet. *Banderilleros* replace them.

The *matador* whose first bull disgraced him walks out, booed by the stands, and I wonder at the courage it took for him to come out again, how he must think, "I will die before I will fail again," how he will wait an extra moment, facing the horns, before he drives the sword home, finding redemption in the blood of his second bull.

The bull makes his first pass, so close that the *matador* brushes against the jellied blood on the bull's back. More passes, then the *matador* strides stiff-legged to the edge of the ring, his back to the bull, where he is handed his sword and another, shorter red cape which he drapes over the blade and faces the bull again. Each pass of the charging, bloody bull seems closer than the last, the *matador's* cape and his glittering "suit of lights" speckled with blood.

Finally, he faces the bull, talking to him, eye to eye, as if they were brothers in this, taking slow steps toward him. "You are a fine bull," he seems to say. "Thank you, my brave brother." He stops a few feet from the bull's horns and calls him. "Come," he says, "now I must kill you."

The bull charges. The *matador* rises to his toes, leans over the bull, and drives the sword up to the hilt, into the bull's heart. The bull stops, the *matador* does not move or pivot away. They seem frozen in a tableau. The assistants rush in, rippling their capes on either side of the bull and he hooks his horns from side to side, the sword blade carving his heart to pieces. Blood begins to flow from his nose and mouth and the *matador* waves off the assistants, walks up, still making eye contact with the bull, and puts his hand on the bull's head, seems to bless him. The bull drops to his knees, vomiting blood, stands up with his last bit of courage and strength, then topples over dead. The *matador* looks down at him, then turns to the cheering crowd who booed him before. . . .

By the time they killed the last bull, the shadow of the arena had moved across the ring like a sundial. The sun was gone now, and dusk was giving way to darkness. I left the arena with everyone else, past the *cerveza* stands, out to the broken streets of Juarez. For a while that night I felt at peace, the way I'd felt when the sun set on those tidal pools in Mendocino. I've given up trying to "explain" my feelings about the bull-fight. Whenever I've tried to do that, people looked at me like I was a monster, the same way they looked at me when I talked about the war none of them had been to. But I feel less crazy, less a monster now, when I think about the bullfights.

Cockfight in Deming
(1984)

A beautiful morning, January 5th, weather in the 60s when we leave the upper valley of El Paso. The Franklin Mountains are pastel pink and orange in the sunlight, cotton and chile fields on either side of the road north. Richard opens a beer, hands me one, lights up a joint, and asks me, "You want any of this blotter acid?"

We stop for Big Macs at the McDonalds in Deming, and ask directions at the Border Cowboy truckstop. Richard had been told that the cockfight was "three or four miles up the old highway." We find the old highway, but after ten miles, no cockfight, so we turn around. "I've never had much luck getting people to tell me where a cockfight is," Richard tells me. Even though cockfighting is still legal in New Mexico, it's kept low profile and word-of-mouth, because the SPCA might lobby the municipal or county government to shut them down.

We stop at a falling-down second hand store, sofas and stuffed chairs propped up off the ground on two-by-fours, and Richard finds a couple of Mexicans out back. They talk in Spanish and English, do a lot of pointing, and we find the place, a big tin building with cars and pickups parked up and down both sides of the road.

We park off the shoulder of the road and walk back to the building, passing a pickup with a woman in the passenger

29

seat, her arms folded across her chest, staring out the windshield. We walk past groups of men tying gaffs on their birds along the side of the building where there are little closets with locks on them, where they keep their birds locked up before the fight, so no one will tamper with them. Each entrant pays $300 to fight six birds—one fight per bird, to the death. There are 35 entrants, the pit takes ten percent, so the winner walks off with about nine-thousand dollars.

Inside I have to pay ten dollars to register as a member of the United Game Fowl Breeders Assn., Inc., two dollars to join the Paisano Game Club, six dollars to get in and two dollars for a reserved seat. A young Mexican in front of me is filling out entrant forms, and the pretty Anglo woman behind the counter tries to explain to him where to put "your name," on the form. "Your name," she says. I point to the line, tell him, "nombre" and he fills it in. A little concession stand behind the ticket counter sells hamburgers, burritos, Cokes and, for a nickel, paper cups so you can take beer into the pit. No bottles are allowed.

The pit seems sinister. It *looks* like something illegal takes place there, devil worship or a freak show. There are actually two pits, side by side, each one about ten feet by twenty, with wooden walls a couple of feet high, and heavy wire six feet above that. The floors are dirt and four parallel lines are scratched into the dirt, the referee using an old broomstick to re-etch the lines between matches.

The seats form a "U" around the pits. They are old theater seats made of plywood, the kind that are attached to each other in rows of six, and they are stacked up in very steep tiers, and aren't anchored as firmly as I would like, rocking whenever anyone stands or sits down. Numbers are hand-painted on the backs. I check the orange ticket the girl pinned on my collar, and we sit in the second of four rows.

Nothing is going on when we sit down. The PA system clicks, whines, the owner of the pit announces, "I got two pits and three referees. I'm payin' 'em good money and I don't want 'em standing around." Before long, entrants show up with their birds.

A short, stocky farm kid, younger than any of the others who are fighting birds, steps into the pit. He wouldn't be bad looking, but his nose has been badly broken, and his whole face looks flat and brutal. His opponent is a Mexican in his late twenties, wearing a goofy derby, obviously his "lucky hat." Early into the match, as the two tried to separate the birds—whenever the birds get tangled up, or one gets his gaff in the other, their handlers very quickly and gingerly immobilize the birds by grabbing them with two hands, then carefully pull them apart—the flat-faced Anglo kid got a gaff driven through the palm of his hand and out the back. Throughout the rest of the fight his hand bleeds, like a stigmata, while he tries to ignore the pain.

Little or no affection is shown by the handlers for their birds. Even in the cockfighting magazines, champion birds are identified only by their breed. The handlers go through their six birds in a businesslike way, *feeding* them into the pit dispassionately, fighting each bird like playing a hand of cards. It seems, too, that people in the seats bet on the *owners* rather than the individual birds, and it makes sense that a rancher from El Paso will have better birds than a poor Mexican from La Unión. The Mexican in the derby loses his 300 bucks, which is a lot of money for him, I imagine. Richard says that these guys *live* for cocking.

While they clean up one ring, a fight begins in the other one. The handlers hold the birds a couple feet apart and let them glare at each other. They cradle the birds in the crooks of their arms, pinning their gaffs, then hold them close enough so they can peck at each other, bite the red "wattle meat" on the sides of their faces, and pull out neck feathers. They hold the birds at their chests and push them at each other, the birds' neck feathers flaring, their wings flapping. Finally, they set the birds down behind the far lines in the dirt and let them go. This is the most beautiful part of the fight, the "buckle." The birds walk to within a couple feet of each other, then *bang,* both of them leap up, feet to feet, off the ground like kickboxers, wings and tails and neck feathers flaring, going at each other with the gaffs. The flared birds are beautiful, more like pheasants than chickens, their colors very "Oriental," luminescent orange and white, greens, blues, purples.

After they separate the birds—like separating boxers in a clinch—the handlers stand them behind the outermost line in the dirt for a count of twenty. While the birds are standing there, the handlers *look* at them, as if they are *willing* them to fight harder, as if they are putting themselves inside the bird, yet there is no feeling of affection for the bird. If the fight has gone on for a while and the bird is hurt and tired, the handler will breathe on the bird, putting his mouth on the bird's back or neck, breathing warm breath into the bird. Some handlers put the bird's beak in their mouths and suck out congestion from the bird, then spit. They stretch the bird's neck, making a straighter airway before they suck. I watched one handler, his bird almost dead from wounds, a particularly bad one at the base of the skull, breathe on his neck, blood showing on the handler's lips until he licked it away. Between "rounds" the ref watches a stop-watch around his neck for a count of 20, begins counting, "17, get 'em ready, 18, 19, pit!" and the handlers push the birds at each other, bumping them together, sometimes talking, "chatting," as they nudge their birds together, almost affectionately, as if the handlers were dancing like a couple.

As I'm watching one of the fights about to begin, I see a flurry of movement to my left and below me, and turn just in time to see a spectator knocked back into a seat, eyeglasses flying. I've noticed him before, shouting bets across the pit, giving odds, keeping track of them in a spiral notebook. He's an Anglo with curly black hair, fashionable horn-rim glasses, jeans and an expensive plaid shirt, in his early thirties. He looks like he might be a guy covering the fight for *Esquire*. Later, Andy tells me that his name is Sidney, and he's a well-known asshole. He used to own a pit in Sunland Park. He built it not a hundred yards from one already there. Then, mysteriously, the original pit caught fire and burned to the ground. Three weeks later *his* pit mysteriously caught fire and burned to the ground.

The man who hit him is a big tough-looking rancher, about my age, with a red beard and a gray cowboy hat with a gold and turquoise gaff pinned to the crown. His hands and face look like they're made out of stone. His nose has a broken hump, his eyes are blue, he has rancher's hands, chapped and scaly, covered with cuts and healing sores. He looks back at "Sidney," who, for a moment, sits up and glares back. The rancher starts to rise from his seat, and Sidney quickly wipes the glare off his face and rids himself of any defensive or aggressive posture. The rancher settles back into his chair, then Sidney stands up and asks him, "Why did you do that?"

"I don't like people to stand in front of me during a fight."

"But the fight hadn't started. I never stand in front of anyone during a fight."

The rancher looks away, and Sidney edges past him and out of the seating area, rubbing his jaw, and trying to look "ironic," having lost an awful lot of face in front of a lot of people. I'm thinking, Jesus, I'd *never* let anybody hit me like that and not jump on him. I'd jump on King Kong if he hit

33

me like that. I'd *die* before I'd be humiliated that way. Then I think, who *gives* a shit what a bunch of people at a cock pit think of me.

The rancher hitting him was like the fighting birds flaring at each other. There is, I realize, sex & violence in the air. I can smell it, feel it in my chest, a combination of beautiful birds cutting and stabbing each other to death, and the hot Hispanic women and blonde Texas Anglo women in tight jeans strutting their stuff. Men in the plywood seats shout bets to each other, collectable on their spoken word alone, passing hundred-dollar bills over the seats with Cokes and hotdogs.

"Boy, howdy," I say to Andy, "there's some hard-faced guys out there."

"What do you expect," he says, "from guys who work shitty jobs all week just so they can watch birds kill each other?"

Not many children to be seen, but it's a family affair in other ways.

An old guy in a wheelchair, both his legs gone at the knee. Two "cowboys," brothers if not twins, about 20 years old, wearing satin jackets and cowboy hats so big that they look goofy. Each hat with a gold #1 badge on the crown. They wear the hats like a challenge, like chips on their shoulders, and it occurs to me that one function of a cowboy hat is to challenge anyone to knock it off your head.

An old couple who *look* like birds, Patriarchs of the Pit, in their seventies–she's wearing white slacks and a red cardigan. She has a lovely brave smile and bird-bright eyes. Her fingers are all crippled up into claws by arthritis, but she's obviously a woman who doesn't complain. During the fights people stop to chat with her and pay their respects. Her husband is tall and thin, like a crane, wearing khaki pants and a denim "sport coat" that is too big for him now that he's gotten so thin. He wears a matching denim baseball cap with the words "Conejo Gin Co." across the crown. His face does not move, only his eyes. His neck is too small for his shirt collar, and his lips are thin. His hands, shaking with tremors, are together in his lap, holding twenty-dollar bills.

An hour or so into the fights Sidney, who has taken some time getting back to his normal enthusiastic self, shouting bets, stops by the rancher and says, "Buy you a cup of coffee?" The rancher turns his head like a turret, shakes his head and looks away. The rancher's wife, obviously very pretty when she was 19 or 20, is chubby now, but content. She's a straw-berry blonde, her hair a practical length, wearing a pink plaid shirt and a pink sweater vest. I've noticed that a lot of people have walked in front of the rancher during fights without any problem, and it's obvious that he just wanted to nail Sidney for some reason.

During the fights, especially when the birds and their handlers first come into the ring, there's lots of shouting, people in the seats standing to call out bets: "I'll lay 50 to 35!" "I'll lay 50-40!" "I like the Black Hat for 50!" (Referring to a handler in a black cowboy hat.) "I'll bet 50-35." "I'll give 10-20." "I got 20 in the pit!" "I bet twenty on the red bird!" "I like the black hat!" All the shouting adds to the atmosphere of close-to-the-surface violence.

During the fight, they stay seated, yelling, *"Kill* that red bird!" or, when one bird is in pretty bad shape, "Sit on 'im, boy!" (Referring to the way a winning bird will come down on top of a disabled bird, striking him with both gaffs, "sitting" on him.)

When one bird is almost dead they move the fight to the two "inside" lines drawn in the dirt. A handler will take a bird that looks dead, stretch its neck, blow on the neck, suck phlegm out of its beak, blow on the back of its neck again. The bird looks dead, a red drop of blood on the tip of its beak and again, here, it's as if the handler has no real affection for the bird, he just feeds it back into the fight like a broken machine. " . . . Seventeen, get ready, eighteen, nineteen, pit!" the reef counts, and the handler drops his bird from knee-height where he's kneeling with him. The bird hits the dirt, rolls onto its back, and kicks a couple of times when the other bird drops down on him–"Sit on that bird!" "Kill that bird!" It's not like a bullfight, the courage of a dying bull that touches everyone watching, it's as if the bird's brainstem is twitching, causing the legs to strike out, the base reflexes, like a chicken with no head. Meanwhile, the spectators are bored with it all, watching the fresh birds in the next pit.

Watching one fight, the birds buckle, and a streak of blood appears on a handler's face. They go at it again, blood is dripping off his hand. The refs re-dig the lines in the dirt now and then, and between fights they clean the feathers up with a leaf rake. At the end of fights, handlers walk off carrying dead birds by the feet, the dead birds, their wings and heads limp, a metaphor for "dejection."

Out of nowhere, between fights, Richard says, "Those Frogs are *hard.* Did you know that if a guy is a real asshole, after they cut his head off with the guillotine, they pick up his severed head and hold it so he can see his headless body?" The cockfights sort of *remind* you of little things like that.

The sun's gone down, cooling off, when we leave the pit. Walking out of the ring, through a long dirt-floored hallway, we pass piles of dead fighting cocks.

"What do they do with the dead birds?" I ask Andy.

"I think there's a market for the feathers."

Richard tells me that Mexicans like knives instead of gaffs, and that Puerto Ricans and Filipinos like long, double-edged

36

knives. He tells me the story about a referee in the Philippines getting his carotid artery slashed by a bird when they buckled.

They're still shouting and betting in the pit as we walk to our car. The woman is still sitting alone in the pickup.

We decide to go to Palomas, "Doves" in Spanish, for supper, just over the border 30 miles away, and stop at a liquor store for another six-pack. I've been nursing my beers, having drunk only about three to Richard's 8 or 10, but the blotter acid Richard took has burned up the alcohol. We find a country & western station on the radio, and Richard asks me if I ever heard George Jones sing, "I Bought the Shoes That Are Walkin' Out on Me."

We are the only Anglos in the Steak House, and we eat at the bar. The dining room has been rented for a *Quinceañera,* a 15th birthday party that also celebrates the transition from girl to womanhood for, in this case, three local girls. They are as beautiful as new brides, dancing in new dresses made for the occasion, an old mirrored ball turning from the ceiling, throwing sparkling light over them, a solemn Mexican band playing slow, sad, romantic songs. A few of the men were at the cockfights, and when they see us they smile, touch the brims of their hats. We smile back. I wonder at the world and the people in it, from savagery to tenderness in a few hours.

We finish our steaks and leave, feeling out of place. On the way out we pay our respects, feeling our way through that wonderful protocol of manners they maintain in Mexico. I feel much better than I did after the cockfights.

The road between Palomas and Deming is the straightest two-lane road I've ever seen. It's up in the high desert where nothing's in the way. For some reason, about midway, there is a long curve, marked with a dozen reflecting orange and black arrows. We pull over to pee. It is cold up there in the high desert after dark, and I listen to the warm engine block of the car go *tic tic tic* as it loses heat. I look up at the sky and see more stars than I've ever seen in my life.

Barranca del Cobre
(1987)

Our first ride, after the train leaves us standing by the empty tracks in Bahuichivo, is a dump truck. It's a *big* dump truck, the kind that eats away the mountains along Interstate 10 in El Paso, digging them out to accommodate shopping malls. We step up on the bolt-studded wheel hub, then on to the top of the tire, up on a step made of welded rebar, then throw our legs over the side of the bed. A family of Tarahumara Indians is already in the truck and they lift our backpacks up and help us in. There are four of us, me and my wife Judith, Barbara, an English teacher at the University of Texas at El Paso, and Dana, a geology graduate student.

The Tarahumara men are dressed in jeans and western-cut shirts, and they all wear straw cowboy hats. Their skin is the color of oiled gunstocks, their hair black, cropped at the collar. They greet us with tentative smiles, then look shyly away. I like them immediately. They remind me of the Montagnard tribesmen I lived with and led on combat operations in Vietnam many years before. Good soldiers. The women wear bright skirts and blouses, turquoise and egg-yolk yellow. One of the younger women looks at herself in the lens of Barbara's mirrored sunglasses, and Barbara helps her try them on. The silver glasses emphasize her high cheekbones, and she could pass for third-world royalty if she were wearing designer jeans and high-heels instead of a handmade cotton skirt and sandals made from truck tires.

The dump truck picks up speed, shuddering and slamming over a road that has been blasted out of the cliffside. I smile at Judith. She grips the side of the truck, knees bent, flexing her legs like a skier as we bounce along. The Tarahumara men bow into the wind, one hand on their hats.

A section of the tailgate has been burned out of the three-quarter-inch steel with a cutting torch, the edge jagged as an ax next to my elbow. The tailgate pounds my kidneys, and I imagine how it would pinch my arms and legs off against the gravel roadbed if the truck turned over. Suddenly I *realize* that I'm in another country, a stoic country, a world without a lifeguard. There are no safety regulations out here in the wilds of Western Chihuahua, no social security or worker's compensation. I shift my weight and glance down at an Indian's sandal-clad foot. It is scarred, a cut on the ankle oozing blood. The foot looks black and hard as iron. An old man, I think, his toothless mouth collapsed. Then I realize that he is probably not much older than I am. The life expectancy of the Indians is 45 years. His life, I think, is harder than mine.

The dump truck comes to the end of the line and we all hand down our packs and bundles and climb down. The four of us turn left, toward the rim of the canyon, while the Indians continue on straight ahead. One of the men turns and smiles, gives us a shy wave, then walks briskly away. I watch him until he is out of sight, a short, bandy-legged man, and I wonder how the world would look to me if I were him. What things would seem important?

That night we camp out by the side of the road, spreading our sleeping bags on pine needles. The land around us looks more like western Montana than Mexico.

The next morning, after coffee around the campfire, we hike down the road toward the rim of the canyon and, we hope, Urique. We're not certain how far it is, or even if we're going the right way, but the day is crisp and clear and I think of the phrase, "a new world every morning." We hear bells up ahead, ringing like wind chimes, and meet a flock of goats tended by a Tarahumara woman and a small boy. *"Buenos dias,"* I say, and she regards us, wary to the point of fear, then says, *"Buenos dias."* The goats break in a wave to let us pass, angling down the hill, their bells clanking.

The goats seem sinister, and I realize why they are often used as devil figures. Their eyes look human, angry at being trapped in an animal's body, burdened with some secret, some terrible truth about the lives of humans and animals.

We hear a truck and music coming our way, and as it rounds the bend behind us I can make out the tune of a popular song, "Dancing in the Dark." The truck is crowded, but the driver offers to take us to Urique for a thousand pesos each, and we wedge ourselves into the back of the pickup. Judith and I introduce ourselves to "Ramon," a young man who is on his way, with his wife and little girl, to visit his mother-in-law. The music is coming from a tape deck slung over his shoulder on a rope. He points at it and says, "Tucson. Tucson, Arizona." He changes tapes for some Mexican ranchero music as we hit the rim of the canyon and start down, the perfect sound-track for our descent.

In an era of hype and televised natural wonders, it is difficult to do justice to the Barranca del Cobre, the Copper Canyon. Had I seen it first in a movie I would have thought it was a trick, a special effect, as it is so beyond the scale of my every-day experience and expectation. Standing in the back of the truck, I look down over the tops of pine trees at the enormous system of canyons opening out and out until they are lost in blue haze nearly seven thousand feet below. It is a view I might expect from the pressurized porthole of an airliner, yet we are traveling over it in a Ford pickup. I think of a mirror-image Shangri-La, ageless and hidden, not in icy Himalayan peaks, but down a tropical valley. The road into the canyon has existed for only ten years. Before that, visitors had to pack in on burros. It is because of this inaccessibility that the Tarahumara have retained their way of life. The rest of the world simply could not get at them. Now, no one expects them to survive much longer, Indians who used to run down deer before the animals were hunted into extinction by outsiders with rifles.

It takes two hours to make the descent to Urique, a village of 200 set into a bend of the Urique River. We can see it more clearly, now on one side of the pickup, then on the other, as we turn from switchback to switchback. The road is narrow and poorly maintained, great bites of it fallen into the canyon. Birds glide above and below us, the air gets warmer, and evergreens are replaced by a species of giant saguaro cactus.

It's siesta time in Urique and its citizens sit on their steps watching us walk past with our aluminum and nylon gear. *"Buenas tardes,"* we say, and *"Hola,"* over and over. The street is made of bowling-ball-size stones set in the dirt, and we share it with dogs, burros, and families of pigs who, noses down, ignore us. The burros stand motionless, angled away as we pass, bony and worn and pot-bellied, paying us no notice, acting as if we were not even there. The street is clean though, patterned into arcing wings by broom strokes. Gardens appear at the edge of town, papaya trees, heavy stalks of bananas, and bamboo trelliswork hung with tomatoes. Green parrots fly squawking overhead. In silhouette they look like flat-nosed ducks.

Thomas Scharman shows us the campground down the hill from his house. He's an American in his late thirties who has lived in Urique for nine years, having fled the pollution of Riverside, California, and the traffic of Pomona. He laughs when he pronounces the name, "Pomona." He has a master's degree in comparative literature. Thomas seems at home here with his wife and two small children, working for the Mexican government to provide health care for the Tarahumara, whose infant mortality rate is between 60 and 80 percent.

The campground is in a grove of mesquite trees, their branches studded with thorns like eight-penny nails. Ian, an Australian on a world tour, steps on a fallen branch while we are there. A thorn pierces his sandal, and he limps for three days. But the trees are in bloom, tiny yellow and white blossoms like fragrant rain, garlanding our hair and floating like stars on the water in our *ollas,* round-bottomed clay pots. A trade-off between threat and beauty.

The river, over the stone fence and across the road from the campground, has a sandy bottom and is full of boulders. The power it develops in the rainy season is obvious in the boulders and tree trunks piled up on the rocky beach. I bathe every morning in the river, and by the end of the week I'm washing my clothes there, beating them against the rocks. I discover the advantage of Ivory soap. It floats.

Grinding stones, powered by wooden paddle wheels, turn steadily, patiently, at the edge of the river, pulverizing handfuls of gold ore. By the end of the week it seems to me that the passage of time in the canyon is marked only by the grinding of the stones and the movement of clouds above the cliffs.

My first night in Urique I discover that it is a "dry" village, alcohol is illegal, and I've been looking forward to a beer for two days. Carlos, a mailman from Chicago who is spending his three-week vacation at the campground, tells me that there

43

is no beer in town, but he knows a house where we can get *tesquino,* a fermented corn beer produced locally.

Like most of the houses in Urique, the *tesquino* house has one wide room in front and two back rooms whose doors are covered with curtains. The *tesquino* is made in the back rooms where they put water and corn in covered *ollas* the size of washtubs and let it ferment.

We must drink it there. The police overlook the operation as long as the drinking is done inside the house. Besides, we find out, the people who make it and the occasional passersby like to drink with you. For 200 pesos, about 40 cents, an old woman brings out a scarred red plastic pitcher which holds about a pint and a half. I share it with Carlos and a couple of local men who drop by. It's not bad tasting at all, sort of malty with an apple taste. It looks like "health food" apple juice, the kind with sediment left in. It seems stronger than beer but not as strong as wine.

Judith, Barbara and Dana stop by, as do Thomas and a dozen local men. We stand in the unfurnished front room, kerosene lamps bouncing shadows off the walls, laughing and talking in clumsy Spanish and English. A heavyset old man with big ears and a whisky-veined nose—I think of Lyndon Johnson—breaks into song, trying hard for quivering low notes. Thomas tells us that the singer is known as "The Dirtiest Man in Urique." He buys hummingbirds from the local children who kill them with slingshots. No one is sure what he does with the tiny green&red birds, but there's a rumor that he grinds them up for some sort of aphrodisiac. While the Dirtiest Man in Urique croons, another man rides up to the door on a white horse, eerie as a ghost in the full moon.

The moon rises late in Urique, having to clear the 7,000-foot canyon walls. When it does rise, it reflects from the cliffs in a dead white glare, brighter than I've ever seen moonlight. The campground is alive with shadows. It is difficult to focus my eyes when I take a midnight walk to the latrine. Shadows seem as solid as the branches and vines along the path. Birds call and roosters crow throughout the night. Dogs howl in the distance, and small animals rustle through the brush. Judith dreams of scorpions, a nightmare about the plates of the earth shifting beneath her.

God, the Tarahumara believe, rules the world during the day and the Devil controls it at night. The sun blesses and the moon threatens. They call the night "the day of the moon" and they fear the souls of the dead who wander the night.

Dawn, too, is late here. There is a pre-dawn, a false dawn, when the din of roosters, the howling and barking of the village dogs echoes through the canyon, chaotic and savage as a painting by Brueghel or Bosch. The canyon seems lost hundreds, even thousands of years in the past.

That afternoon I climb up behind the campground, pulling myself up at first by grabbing shrubs and tree limbs. I edge and duck my way through thorns and underbrush until I break into the open. A burro trail snakes up the mountain, vanishing at times, washing out over the rocks, but I settle into a brisk uphill pace, stopping to look behind me at the river, farther and farther below. When I finally glance at my watch, I discover that I've been climbing for over an hour. The river is far below and I am very much alone. The sound of my own breathing seems thunderous. Buzzards circle in the thousands of feet of empty air between me and the top of the canyon, and I can see silver leaves from trees on the canyon rim as they sideslip in and out of the sun, slow and erratic and relentless as time. Dark high clouds are pushing over the cliffs, and I can hear the wind, high up there in the rimrock. I put my hands against the stone on which I'm kneeling, and fight down my fear.

What, I think, what if I had been born a Tarahumara in this savage canyon? What would the world, the brutal indifference of these cliffs look like to me? How would I understand life and death, work and love? I know nothing, I think, nothing at all.

I reach down and pick up a red pebble. I hold it between my thumb and finger, then touch it to my cheek. I will take the pebble back home and when my life seems confusing and complicated, I will take it out and hold it and remind myself of this world.

I slip it into my pocket and climb down toward the river.

Making War,
Not Love
(1980)

The First Annual Soldier of Fortune Convention swept into Columbia, Mo., like a little hit of acid cut with speed, a drugged memory of the sixties, a tinny old Dylan song. There were 800 camouflaged conventioneers, 60 media people from as far away as Paris, and a handful of protesters–bearded young men with earnest, born-again eyes, carrying signs that pro-claimed, "Soldiers of Fortune=Mercenaries=Hired Killers." One of the protesters wore a chrome-plated police whistle round his neck and carried marking pens and chemical Mace in his Levi's. "We're against these mercenaries," he said, "because they kill for money and adventure. And they have a right-wing ideology."

The townspeople were not happy about the event, which was sponsored by the magazine *Soldier of Fortune.* A local restaurant posted a sign saying that mercenaries would not be served there. A coed told me, "I feel like we've been invaded by a bunch of grown men playing soldier." An editorial in the Columbia *Missourian* referred to the conventioneers as "the sick and the deluded," a group of "pus-flecked souls." And at a faculty cocktail party a Shakespeare professor declared over his bourbon, "They've got rocks in their heads."

The action was at Ray Chapman's shooting academy, a few miles outside of town, where 100 shooters were participating in the first annual *Soldier of Fortune* three-gun combat match. But most of the conventioneers ignored the match, the occasional pop of handguns and crack of assault rifles in the background. It was the convention exhibit hall that got the crowds. You could buy customized forty-fives, handmade combat knives, $3,000 rifle laser sights, T-shirts that proclaimed "Death to Tyrants" and "Peace Through Superior Firepower," manuals on everything from illegal entry to *How to Kill* (Volumes I-IV), night-vision devices and electronic bugs, Nazi memorabilia, and posters that asked, "PARANOID? Most of your fears are real." Skills, equipment, and black humor I hadn't been around since I was mustered out of Special Forces ten years ago.

There were loonies and losers and loud talkers playing to the media and posing with guns and knives, but the convention was dominated by Vietnam veterans who had come to look for old friends and to talk about old times. Many of them had fought with elite units—Marine Force Recon, Special Forces— genuine bad-asses who were responsible for an atmosphere of simple good manners in the crowd. People were quick to say "excuse me" if they accidentally jostled someone. Most of the people at the convention seemed to realize that if anyone started trouble, it could get very serious in a hurry. I overheard one man tell a friend, "Walk softly. This isn't the place to kick sand in anybody's face."

The cocktail hour at the Hilton Hotel came, and I found myself talking to a group of soldiers, both active and retired. They were the real thing. They had limps and wound scars, and some of them had done double and triple tours of duty in Vietnam, the kind of men who keep their word when they give it and make hard decisions when they have to. I hadn't seen their kind for a long time, and I discovered that I had missed their honesty and brutal humor. I drank with them and swapped war stories.

And then suddenly it was 2:00 A.M. in the Flaming Pit lounge. The cocktail hour had been going on a long time. The bar was crowded with men, most of them in their early thirties, wearing camouflage fatigues and jungle boots. The guy across the table from me, the one wearing a drill instructor's widebrim hat, didn't like my act at all. He didn't like the way I had my hair pulled back with a black bandanna; he didn't like the fact that I was wearing a press pass, and he didn't like the way I was cheerfully ignoring his hostility.

At a glance, he seemed relaxed, his eyes hidden beneath the brim of his brown hat, but if you looked closely you could see that he was sitting on the edge of his chair, half his weight tensed on his legs, ready to come across the table at me. I was enjoying it. The combination of liquor and adrenaline had cranked the scene into an amphetamine-like high of sharp focus and glib self-confidence.

"So then," I asked him, smiling, "what did you think about the banquet speech tonight?"

"Not a *damn* thing."

"Well then," I said to the man on my right, "what did *you* think– "

"You know *why* I didn't think anything about the speech?" the guy in the hat demanded.

"No, I don't. Why was it?"

"Because when they were giving the speech, I was out on some goddamn dirt road, throwing fists. See that?" he said, looking at me *hard* and pointing to a cut under his eye, "I was out getting that, and I'm proud of it. At least I found somebody who didn't mind trading fists. If you know what I mean."

"Right. I guess you got hit there. Under the eye. Anyway, how far did you come for the convention?"

"Gastonia, North Carolina. A place you've never been."

"See there," I said, with a nasty smile, "you're wrong. I know Gastonia. It's a mean little town about forty miles from where I was born. Kind of a little strip-town off the highway. I always used to lock the doors of my car whenever I had to drive through there—past all the Dari-Treets and Bob's Burgers, right? People in Gastonia didn't like my looks." I asked a conventioneer on my left, "What did you think about the banquet?"

"What do *you* think about *this,* motherfucker?" the guy in the hat asked, and pulled out a revolver. He pointed it across the table at my face. "What do you think?" he said. The men on either side of me sat very still. The live local band plugged along. "What do you think?" he asked.

I shook my head and then said, a little sadly, "I think it's pretty cheap behavior."

The gun stayed there in my face for a moment; then he put it away. He glared at me and said, "I guess I'll get out of here." He rose and started to go, then turned and said, "Unless you want to step outside with me for a minute."

"No," I said, "I don't want to."

Suddenly, I felt bad about the convention, about the guy in the hat, and about myself. The war was over a long time ago. "Hey," I said, "sit down. I was *there, I . . . .*

"I don't care where you were, man," he said. He turned and left.

The bar was closing, so I walked out to the parking lot with the man who'd been sitting to my right, a pleasant guy who had only a first name, "Jim," on his nametag. "I liked that," he said, " 'Pretty cheap behavior.' I'll have to add that to my list of comebacks to people who pull guns on me. You know, along with the standards—like falling down on the floor and throwing up."

When Jim walked, he pulled his right leg along, locked at the knee. The parking lot was almost empty.

"You got a little limp there. Your leg must have gone to sleep in the bar," I said, trying to joke, I guess, trying to make some contact, trying to salvage something.

"Yeah. My third tour over there I had an accident. They mailed me home." He was silent. Then he said, "You know what pissed me off? You get back home, and they want to buy you a drink. I didn't want a drink, I had money. I could have bought the whole bar a *drink.*"

Night Maneuvers
(1981)

W e are living in Babylon," the preacher declared from his plywood podium, "and it is going to fall just like it did before. We have to get out of the cities, and we have to get the cities out of us. We will have one hour. It tells us that in Deuteronomy."

It was no ordinary revival. There was more than the usual religious fervor at this gathering of the Christian Patriots. The worshipers were not typical. One bearded man was dressed all in black. Another was wearing a black beret and a T-shirt with a picture of a robed Klansman on a rearing white horse surrounded by flames. A young woman in camouflage fatigues sported a silver death's head belt buckle the size of my fist. A pale, blond-haired man in wraparound sunglasses looked like a cross between a rock star and a Hitler youth. And a burr-headed fat kid of twelve, the kind of kid who looks like he tortures cats, had a World War I trench knife on his belt, the type with brass knuckles built into the handguard. Half the people in the tent wore camoflauge fatigues, and almost everyone was wearing some kind of knife—sheath knives, boot knives, folding fighter knives, belt-buckle push daggers, stilettos in fancy shoulder rigs—expensive weapons designed to kill people.

More men in fatigues and berets stood around the tent. They wore forty-fives in shoulder holsters and carried assault rifles, twelve-gauge riot guns, and automatic weapons on assault slings. The red-white-and-blue insignia on their uniforms was a cross overlaid with sword and battle-ax. They were members of the training cadre from The Covenant, The Sword, The Arm of the Lord, a survival school, who were going to lead the night class on a simulated combat patrol. Most of the cadre live on a 200-acre base near the Arkansas-Missouri border. The base is fortified with bunkers, tunnel complexes, and a twenty-four-hour perimeter defense, and the cadre live in a state of readiness, we were told, as if the "collapse" had already occurred.

"Just one hour, people," the preacher continued, "to fight, resist, and flee. Already concentration camps are being prepared to hold Christians. There is a one hundred-million-acre compound in Alaska, one of several in the country. We have to be ready to fight, people, but weapons without God are vanity. But God . . . God can give us 223s, 308s, or he can give us the jawbones of asses. It don't matter, because He wants us to see Israel, the true Israel.

"People, I don't want to see your babies tossed around on the tips of bayonets. I don't want to see your women raped–forty times in one night. I don't want your children molested by homosexuals. So tonight we are going to begin preparing ourselves for what is to come. They're watching us. The enemy is watching us–we know who they are–and they want to stop what we're trying to do here. But we will use what we can. I know that none of us has been in a war, in combat. We don't really know what it will be like, but we will use what we can to help us prepare for it.

"Lord, help us to do thy will tonight. Help us learn the skills of combat patrolling and be with us in tonight's operation. Amen."

I'd arrived that morning at the estate grounds, fifty-five acres in central Illinois, the entrance only a couple of blocks from the courthouse in Louisville. A banner over the gate proclaimed, "Welcome Patriots." A security man stepped out of the guardhouse to check the attendance reservation I'd gotten in the mail that stipulated: "Admission is conditioned [sic] upon the bearer being of the White (Caucasian) Race."

The guard, who was carrying an AR-18 assault rifle and who had the current issue of *Soldier of Fortune* magazine tucked beneath his arm, waved me into a parking area.

The convention site was pleasant, grassy and well kept, dotted with groves of trees, hills and meadows, and even a lily pond complete with geese. The "headquarters building," a barnlike duplicate of George Washington's Mount Vernon and built, for some reason, 20 percent larger than the original, was in need of paint. It housed display booths where you could buy freeze-dried foods, survival books and pamphlets, army training manuals, army-surplus combat gear, aluminum blowguns, bulletproof vests, Ku Klux Klan T-shirts and pocket knives, bumper stickers that declared, in red-white-and-blue, "Joe McCarthy Was Right," "Unleash our Energy—More Nukes NOW," "Anglo Power," "Stop E.R.A.," or "I Won't Give Up My Gun Till They Pry It from My Cold, Dead Fingers," and books on everything from surviving nuclear war to avoiding payment of income tax. There were literally tons of pamphlets with titles like "The Jewish World Conspiracy," "Jewish Ritual Murder," and "The Anita Bryant Story." Another pamphlet, "How to Deal with Niggers," offered a list of rules that included the advice "Never engage them in debate or conversation. Nothing a nigger knows or thinks is of the slightest importance to you." There were dozens of pamphlets "proving" that the Holocaust never happened and that the Jews are barbarian impostors, that the true Israelites–God's chosen people–are all white, Anglo-Saxon Americans.

The Freedom Festival participants were utterly humorless. The only times I heard laughter were when someone told a racist joke. These were mostly blue-collar people who had worked hard and, not getting their share of the American dream, were looking for scapegoats to blame their problems on, Jews and blacks. They reminded me of Germany before Hitler came to power–people looking for a cause: a leader, and for self-respect.

At a seminar on small-unit tactics conducted by a general, a stocky woman in her fifties stood up, looked around, and said, "I don't know if there are any spies here, but why don't we just eliminate some of the leaders like Kissinger and Rockefeller instead of just waiting for it to happen?" People in the crowd chuckled and nodded their heads, and the general said, "Well, it isn't that a lot of us haven't thought about it, but this isn't a class on assassination."

At that point I was acutely aware of an armed security cadre standing behind me, and I decided then to use a much smaller notebook and to use a pseudonym for this article.

The Christian Patriots believe–and they hope–that one or more of the following will happen: The Communists will invade the United States from Cuba, Mexico, and Canada. The economy will collapse, and traitors within our own government will precipitate a nuclear war. The cities will go up in fire storms, and marauding hordes of blacks will flee the cities to loot, rape, and murder. Whichever, the Christian Patriots will establish an area in the Midwest, where they will hold off the hordes and survive. This area will be a "Golden Triangle, the true Jerusalem," as foretold by George Washington after he was granted three visions by an angel at Valley Forge.

56

After the prayer, the cadre lined up into columns of twelve to fifteen people. I looked over at a high school kid in the next column and saw that he had an automatic pistol in a fancy cross-draw holster. As I watched, he pulled the pistol out and fumbled with it for a full minute, trying to cock it or put the safety on or off or something. He clearly didn't know what he was doing. I'd thought that only the cadre would have weapons, but as I looked around, I saw that I was wrong. Half the people in the class were armed. They had shotguns, pistols, and sophisticated assault rifles on their persons.

And then I saw a pretty girl I'd seen that afternoon in the small unit tactics class, a cute brunette who'd been wearing a "White Power" button. Now she was wearing camouflage fatigues and carrying a short-barreled .12 gauge riot gun. I had an impulse to go over to her and say, "Hey, why don't we knock off this silly shit? Let's go somewhere and talk or something." But she had that *look* on her face, just like the others. They were *serious*. They thought that this was the real stuff. They'd all read their training manuals, but none of them knew that once the shooting starts, all the rules go out the window.

We were told that the evening's exercise was to teach us to "get down" quickly when fired at by the enemy. When the squad leader fired his rifle into the air, we were to fall down, facing alternately left and right. Abruptly, the speaker fired his rifle, having braced it casually against his hip. Some of the participants fell quickly in the correct direction, some of them in the wrong direction, while others crouched, looked around, and then went down on all fours while a few just remained standing, hunched over and confused.

"All right, people," the squad leader shouted, "that was pretty slow. When you hear a shot, you get *down*. You don't have time to think about it. You think about it, and you're gonna be dead. Okay. Everybody back up. Let's try it again."

He fired again, and again, until almost everyone was falling quickly and in the correct direction. The overall military commander of the Christian Patriots walked among the participants, carrying a stick. He was wearing a khaki uniform with red shoulder boards. He had a total of twenty silver stars on his two shoulders, and enough stars, crossed swords, and enameled brass badges on his beret to pass as an Eagle Scout at a national jamboree or as the star of a Gilbert and Sullivan musical. He rapped people's heels with the stick after they fell, telling them, "Get those heels down." There seemed to be some confusion as to whether the heels should be turned in, out, or to one side to avoid, I suppose, serious heel wounds.

Finally, the columns "moved out" toward a pasture, falling whenever the squad leader fired into the air. It was dusk, and for a few minutes I tried to pretend that I was back in Vietnam, heading for a night location, but the whole business was so absurd that I gave it up. One enthusiastic trainee rolled behind a patch of weeds after falling and was singled out and praised by the squad leader for his imagination and quick thinking. I kept wondering, "Don't these people realize that it's fine to fall down when you're shot at, but after that you are going to have to do something?"

By the time it was dark, we were lying prone in the grass, sweating, while the mosquitoes bit hell out of our necks, wrists, and ankles. Women and children were clustered around a couple of cars behind us while the cadre split into two groups to simulate a firefight and "give us some idea of what it's like to be in combat."

The guy next to me wanted to low-crawl through the grass, get behind the cadre, and "ambush" them. I declined to go with him, and he seemed disappointed in my lack of enthusiasm.

And then the firefight began. The two groups fired bottle rockets–those little firecrackers attached to slivers of wood– at each other and threw strings of firecrackers. For ten minutes the rockets hissed through the air, whistled, cracked and popped, turned into green and red pin wheels, and spun in the grass, throwing sparks. It was a pretty enough display but not like any firefight I've ever been in. Both sides yelled racial insults at each other in the dark, "Come and get it, nigger!" "Come on, jigaboo!" "Eat that, spear chuckers!" The guy who'd wanted to ambush the cadre giggled and said, "I hope that reporter from Boston isn't still here."

Out in the dark someone yelled, "Two things you can't give a nigger–a fat lip or a black eye." The crowd thought that was a good one. I heard the women and children laughing back by the cars. One of the women yelled, "Take his ears. Take his ears," and that got more laughs.

After the firefight, the cadre offered up a prayer, thanking God for allowing us all to "successfully complete this training exercise without anyone being injured."

I went back the next morning, There was a light rain falling, and most of the people with exhibit booths had packed up their stuff and left. A Christian self-defense group was practicing the "overhand nose smash" in the drizzle, shouting as they slammed their fists down in unison. As I walked back to my car, I noticed the general looking out at the rain from behind a screen door in the 20 percent-larger-than-the-original replica of Mt. Vernon. He seemed to represent the spirit of the place. Inept, confused, and unutterably *sad*.

Call It
Neglect of Duty
(1983)

This summer in Berkeley, California, I went to a special showing of the World War II combat saga *The Big Red One*. Samuel Fuller, the writer-director of the film, talked about it afterward. He said that he had tried not to show any emotion more than once, tried not to repeat himself in the movie.

"What about the emotion you feel," I asked him, "when you kill someone who was trying to kill you, and you stand there, looking down at this dead guy, thinking, 'I'm alive and he's nothing,' and you feel great?"

Fuller thought a moment. "That's not in this movie," he said, "but that's the most honest emotion that comes out of war."

It is an emotion, born of terror and rage, that the producers of CBS's *Tour of Duty* have chosen to avoid. *Tour of Duty's* Sergeant Anderson (played by Terence Knox) should know that emotion, but he doesn't. He is too nice, too even-tempered, too compassionate for a soldier in his third combat tour. No one volunteers for two extra years of combat unless he *likes* the risk, the adrenaline, the killing. The soldiers in Sergeant Anderson's platoon are nice kids, even the swaggering Puerto Rican machinegunner (Ruiz). And the angry black street kid (Taylor) never does anything worse than glare and grumble about following orders. Through firefight after firefight, they remain nice kids, shocked by brutality and concerned for the safety of Vietnamese civilians. That's a comforting concept of human nature, but it's not true.

Soldiers are not the same after a couple of fire fights. They change. They go to sleep scared every night and wake up exhausted and afraid at dawn, day after day. They stop being nice kids and become killers because that's the only way to stay alive. Life is simple out on patrol. You march beyond exhaustion, eat and sleep when you can and kill *anything* that threatens you.

The soldiers in the series don't look *scared* on patrol most of the time: it's as if they somehow forgot about the armed men out there trying to kill them. In one episode, Sergeant Anderson and two of his men have been shot down, one of them painfully burned, deep in enemy-controlled territory. They know the enemy is after them, close behind. Yet they stop and risk exposing themselves to "help" a woman giving birth. When she dies, they take the baby and amble down a trail, talking, laughing and singing "Rockabye Baby." They enter an enemy-controlled village, steal a goat from a comical, broom-swinging Vietcong woman and take it—bleating and braying—with them into the jungle where there's some cute business about milking it into a canteen for the baby. I'm willing to accept some distortion of reality to accommodate plot development, but I could no longer take this episode seriously. These guys are in deep trouble. They should be moving fast and quietly, staying off trails and out of sight.

If I were the producer, I'd want to hire four or five thugs to hang around the set, lifting weights and glaring at the cast. I'd send them in to slap and punch the actors around. It could happen any time the actors were resting, eating or doing a scene. The thugs might return in five minutes or five days.

The actors' fear of these random assaults would, in a small way, approximate the fear that's always there on patrol.

The theatrical movie *Platoon* was vivid and convincing because the actors were exhausted and filthy and harassed. Dale Dye, the technical adviser, and his staff spent two weeks with them before filming began. The actors slept in foxholes, ate cold rations and went on forced marches through the Philippine jungle with full packs. They were tormented and screamed at day and night, their sleep interrupted by grenade simulators. They looked and acted like combat veterans by the time filming began.

Dye was initially hired to oversee the production of *Tour of Duty*. After some pre-production work, however, he was called in and told that "a decision had been made" to use Department of Defense advisers. The upside of DOD advisers is that the production company gets helicopters and equipment and assistance at bargain rates. The downside is that the scripts are subject to scrutiny by the DOD. These are people who, during the war, changed the term "search and destroy" to "search and clear" when Americans, seeing bodies and burned villages on the 6:30 news, began to consider the implications of the word "destroy." The people who "neutralized" Communist cadres, "sanitized" after-action reports, exaggerated body counts and kept telling us we were winning the war we were losing. Do you think they are going to deal in the truth now when they have a chance to tidy up history and present a "positive image" of the Army?

Tour of Duty should get rid of the Department of Defense and the compromises involved. Give them back their helicopters. The show doesn't need all those choreographed helicopter sequences like car chases in detective shows.

We need fewer jungle shoot-outs and more character development. These guys have to *change*. They have to get harder, stop saying, in dismay, things like, "Who could have *done* this? These are just *civilians,*" when they come across dead villagers. Dead civilians were commonplace, killed by accident and on purpose by both sides all the time. The three best episodes introduced strong characters–a tortured Special Forces soldier, a brave but racist black combat veteran on his second tour, and an alcoholic hero–but they were largely wasted on awkward plots and then eliminated at the end of the hour. A more open-ended plot structure would allow the producers to develop characters through more than one hour.

And they can't ignore obvious tactical realities. In episodes I've seen, Anderson's platoon never seems to put out security when they set up camp on operations. They are as casual as campers in a state park. After firefights they stand around as if nothing much had happened–back to normal, not worried that the people who were shooting at them might start shooting again. Why aren't they quivering with adrenaline? Why aren't they securing their perimeter and sending out reaction forces to kill the people who shot at them? It made me wonder if any of the DOD advisers were ever in combat in Vietnam.

Worried that I was being unreasonable, that these inaccuracies didn't matter, I showed a couple of episodes to the students in the "Literature of the Vietnam War" class I taught at the University of Texas. The students, who know nothing about military tactics, spotted most of the problems as lapses in common sense. One of them said, "It's just another TV show, like *Lost in Space,* except they're wearing helmets and carrying M-16s." Until recently, the producers were working against a "family viewing" time slot that restricted realistic language and the amount of violence they could portray. They are on a very tight production schedule, cranking the shows out if they want to stay on the air, with little time for long-term planning. And they have another problem. Americans, after all, may not want the truth about the war. They may not honestly believe the truth when they see it.

Gustav Hasford, whose novel *The Short-Timers* was the basis for the theatrical movie *Full Metal Jacket,* was once told by an editor that he'd have to do a major rewrite of his book; otherwise, "people think that Marines are nothing but trained killers." That, of course, *is* what they are. Another editor suggested that I invent childhood traumas to "explain" why the soldiers in my Vietnam novel, *Sympathy for the Devil,* are so brutal. He couldn't understand that constant exposure to violent death will turn anyone brutal if he hopes to stay sane and alive. Most Americans have never been physically assaulted—except, perhaps, for a junior-high-school shoving match—much less afraid for their lives. Certainly they've never been afraid of being killed, day after day, for months. That kind of fear, and the brutal rage that grows from it, is an emotion as unexpected and fundamental and powerful as love. But how do you produce love stones for an audience that has never been in love? That is the problem facing *Tour of Duty*.

"Introduction" to
TRIPS by Charles Fischer
(1994)

Drugs have gotten a bad reputation in the 90s. Students in my fiction classes at the university describe a character as being "on drugs," and think that defines him, that all drugs are equally devastating and people who "do" drugs are all alike. They call the blind man who smoked his first joint in Raymond Carver's wonderful story, "Cathedral," a *dope addict*.

"Drug Free Zone" warnings ring the suburban public schools, as if swarthy "pushers" are watching the playgrounds, waiting for recess to sell joints and heroin and rocks of crack to freckled third-graders for their lunch money and "hook" them forever. These same kids, earnest and clean-cut, collecting money to *fight* drugs, ring my doorbell when I'm eating supper. I keep the door wide open and step outside so no one can accuse me of being a child molester, while they hurry through the speech they've memorized, selling candy or raffle tickets or a ribbon to tie on my car's radio antenna to declare that I, too, am *against drugs*.

When they leave I go back to my supper and six o'clock news footage of DEA SWAT teams in Ninja costumes assaulting crack houses, sending more black men to prison at enormous cost to taxpayers, where they *can't take drugs,* by God. They chose a "drug lifestyle" instead of, say, choosing to attend law school, and now they're paying for it. Drugs have become our scapegoat, our explanation of why things are not so good in America anymore, our excuse for ignoring the poverty and despair of the inner cities.

Watching the news I think back to when I was a cop working the streets of North Portland and, ten years later, East Oakland. My partner and I tried to avoid any contact with narcs, not wanting the neighborhood to think we might be working together. But I recall one night when we had to provide backup for a couple of narcs, waiting with them in a seedy rooming house, a toilet running in the common bathroom down the hall. The room smelled of old sweat, stale cigarette smoke, rotting food and roach spray. I stood in a corner and looked at the *Playboy* centerfold taped to the wallpaper over the bed while they dumped dresser drawers, finding, among other things, a single hypodermic needle and a page of newspaper want-ads, "Janitor" and"Busboy" circled in felt-tip pen.

"What did I tell you?" one of them said to me, holding the needle up.

"Oh no," I said, throwing my arms out, "it's proof. This guy uses illegal drugs." I stepped closer and told him, "You know what? If I had to live in a dump like this, I'd shoot as much heroin as I could find."

"You're fucked up, man," the other one, a weightlifter with a ponytail, said. "John's right. You're fuckin' weird."

"And you're fuckin' dumb as they come," I told him.

"*Fuck* you," he said, taking a step toward me.

"Fuck *you*, stupid," I said.

My partner stepped between us, and after we were back on the street, he and I laughed about the importance of communication.

The news is interrupted by commercials for Anacin, Advil, Mylanta, Tums, Sominex, middle-aged actors hollow-eyed with insomnia and work-related stress, staggering through blinding headaches, heartburn, irregularity and sinus pain, until they take a pill that renders them serene as a heroin fix would, able to "enjoy life again."

Late night TV is all public service ads fighting drugs, no matter that few people see them. "This is your brain on drugs." All the campaigns and drives and marches against drugs seem to have worked here in the vast Middle America, where I live now, but it doesn't seem like a better place.

It was a different world back in the '60s when LSD came on the scene. Drugs were an adventure for young men and women, like skydiving or mountain climbing, a way to challenge your own fear. Some died, more the result of daring and recklessness than the drugs themselves, kids who might have been killed in drunken car wrecks or in that war we had going.

While young Americans died in Vietnam of gunshot and shrapnel wounds, friendly fire and helicopter crashes, back in the world musicians and hippies and runaways were ODing on drugs. Often it was the best and brightest who died. Jimi Hendrix, a genius who could never have written that music without the LSD and heroin that killed him. Would he have given the music up to live seventy years clean and sober? Janis Joplin, singing her life away. Jim Morrison, overdosing in a bathtub in Paris, a middle-class kid who could have been a medivac pilot bringing his Huey into another hot LZ, green 12.7mm tracers swarming out of the tree line into his Plexiglas windshield.

As the war escalated I took LSD, direct from Timothy Leary's commune at Millbrook, so new it wasn't even illegal yet, the workaday rituals and moral injunctions of society suddenly absurd through my dilated eyes. I'd paint my face with little tins of greasepaint, green and blue tiger-stripes with black cheekbones, or solid white so my teeth and eyeballs looked yellow and wolf-like, and ride my motorcycle through town, laughing, my pupils huge and black, the headlights of oncoming cars boiling like atomic furnaces. My drug of choice in Vietnam was army-issue pharmaceutical methamphetamine. We had a flesh-colored plastic half-gallon jar of them on top of the refrigerator in the team house: "Special Forces popcorn." It made me more enthusiastic about going out in the dark to kill people, and I fell in love with the war, certain it would kill me.

When I came home and became a cop, my drugs of choice were adrenaline, beer and shots of Irish whisky. Legal and far more dangerous than those other drugs, the liquor almost killed me a few years later. One of my old partners, a homicide detective now, thought that we drank to maintain the adrenaline high we brought to the police bar after work every night. I got to where I could tell, just by the way someone walked, that he was ready for a fight. All I had to do was call out to him, "Excuse me, sir. Could I talk to you for a moment?" and before long, I'd be fighting him to the street, choking him out in a rush of sweet adrenaline.

I can't recommend drugs to anyone, any more than I can recommend going to war. I'm lucky to be alive, yet those days were rich with life, risk, self-knowledge and smiling death, my companion and teacher. Perhaps it's morally superior to just "say no" all your life, then rot in a nursing home or end up sucking on Dr. Kevorkian's carbon monoxide bottle, but I don't think so.

Charles Fischer is lucky to be alive, too, surviving the years testing mega-doses of LSD, trading food stamps for mescaline and angel dust, eating psilocybin in Montana bars. The stories in *Trips* are the best written, most articulate and intelligent "drug stories" I know of, the terrors of PCP rushes, of losing control, hallucinations remembered almost fondly, the way old soldiers recall the chaos of combat, survival a matter of dumb luck and keeping their nerve. Most of the good drug stories never got written and are lost forever. Fischer is one of the few who survived the drugs and the lonely years, learning to write, brave and honest enough to tell us the truth. A good soldier.

Sturgis

(1989)

Thursday night flight from Denver to "Rapid," what the locals call Rapid City, in a 40 passenger twin turbo prop ATR 42. New Line Cinema sending me to the annual biker run in Sturgis, South Dakota to do research for a script I'm writing.

Everyone on the little plane nervous as the engines rev and we take off, slowly gain altitude, shuddering and bobbing as we skirt huge thunderheads that rise from the earth, then flatten out, full of black holes of wind, the flash-glow of lightning like exploding artillery rounds deep inside. The plane seems tiny and vulnerable. More turbulence. Passengers trying not to show fear. There have been a lot of plane crashes this summer.

Reading lights on Stetsons and seed-corn hats, the hum and buzz of the props, the strobe light flashing along the wing as regular as a pulse. A tension and intimacy among the passengers you don't feel in the big jets. It's like a stage set, and I think of John Wayne whistling the theme to "The High and the Mighty" as he limps off his C-47.

A woman in the seat in front of me is reading *People* magazine, a piece about Ed McMahon's failed marriage. LA and Hollywood seem far away, and I realize that I'm happy, or content at least, for now. The plane reminds me of all those flights in DC3s with my mother and baby sister when I was a kid, off to another air force base to meet my father.

After LA, the highways below seem lonely, farmhouse guard lights, cross-country trucks, a car on one of the farm roads turning its lights on in the serene blue twilight. From 24,000 feet I watch the big circular irrigated fields and clustered lights of farm towns appear then slip beneath the wing of the plane.

It gets darker as we fly over the more barren badlands. Towns and farms can only exist where there is water. Trees grow thick along the rivers that finger out into deltas, giving them a fernlike appearance. Now the dark land could be an ocean, the lights fishing boats and freighters. At one point I can see two little towns, maybe 40 miles apart, and I imagine a kid from one of them driving across the dark farmland, dust in his headlights, to see a girlfriend in the next town.

Our flight attendant looks like a farm girl and tries to *sound* like a flight attendant on a big jet, that phony "up" tone and rhythm, her voice cracking with static over the PA system. "For those of you. Continuing. On to Pierre. . . . "

At the Rapid City airport I have a couple of beers and wait for the Hell's Angels who are supposed to meet me here. I ask the three middle-aged men and the early-20s barmaid about the Sturgis biker run. "Well, you know there's a difference between 'bikers' and 'motorcycle riders.' About ninety percent of 'em are just motorcycle riders who have regular jobs and families. But these people at Sturgis tend to be the type who like to wear black leather. A few years ago they took over Deadwood. Raped three girls. And they had to call in the Highway Patrol and the National Guard to get them out. One guy got killed." When the men go back to watching the football game on TV, the barmaid comes over and tells me how she enjoys the run, the excitement. The Angels don't show, so I rent a car and stop at Wendy's for a burger and ask the two kids behind the counter for directions to Sturgis. The girl is corn-fed chunky, the boy a nice kid–they seem more wholesome than the poor minority kids who work the burger joints in the city–and they both think the run is neat, "about the biggest thing that happens around here." They ask me where I'm from. When I tell them, "LA," they grin and give me a "thumbs up." On the way out I double-check directions–which exit to take–with a tall, confident kid who just walked in with his date. He looks like a "popular" senior who probably lettered on the basketball team. He tells me that they just got back from Sturgis. It's a daring thing for the local kids to do. Drive up and watch the bikers.

I make the 30 mile drive up Highway 90 to Sturgis. Motor-cycles thunder around me, carloads of local high school kids pass me doing 80 in tinny little cars with four or five drunk kids inside, bopping their heads to the radio. The bikers, in comparison, seem somber in goggles and bandannas, careful to obey the speed limit. Way up ahead on the dark highway I see their amber turn signals blinking as they pass older, bigger, slower cars, which they refer to as "cages." The rolling thunder of bikes goes on day and night.

I turn off the interstate and drive into town on a pleasant tree-lined road, surrounded by motorcycles, passing old stone houses, seedy little motor courts, a double-garage with the hand-lettered sign, "Showers–6 A.M. to midnight." I park on a side road next to a church and walk two blocks to Main Street, which is blocked off to cars. It's about eleven and things are going strong. Main Street looks like a frontier town that's been "modernized." Flat midwest storefronts that are mostly empty all year except for when the biker run is in town. The Norwest Bank building looks out of place, modern in that steel siding/plate glass way, as does the "BHP" (Black Hills Power and Light). The Ben Franklin store has a handlettered sign "Welcome Bikers" taped to the front window. Paklin Shoe Repair. Town&Country Plumbing. Hog Brothers (a biker store there year round). The Oasis Bar and Lounge. Gunner's Lounge.

Temporary "beer gardens" have been set up in vacant lots. Hamburger stands, taco stands, hot dog stands. Lots of T-shirt vendors. Gutted storefronts with rows of folding tables full of custom motorcycle parts, T-shirts, leather clothes. Most of them with two, three, four tattoo artists at work in back, the electric buzzing of tattoo needles constant as the rumble of bikes.

The five-block long main street is wide. Four rows of bikes parallel-parked in the middle. A single row of parked bikes along the flanking sidewalks, the street still wide enough for wagons and horses. An endless loop procession of bikes up and down the street, racing engines, showing off, girls on P-pads leaning back against sissy bars. I talk to some bikers from Nebraska and one tells me how his old lady hates to ride on the P-pad because the bruises it makes on her ass show when she wears short-shorts. Thousands of motorcycles cruising up and down the street, day and night, the street slick with hot oil, sunlight, then headlights flashing off the chrome and custom paint jobs. Beautiful machines.

A tattoo parlor below street level. Two girls behind the fence-like barrier are getting tattoos while a dozen other people watch. One is a fat girl with bleached blond hair wearing a tank top, the words "Evil Wicked Mean and Nasty" already tattooed across her tits. She's smoking a cigarette and working hard at looking relaxed as the bearded tattoo artist works on her calf. He pulls down the jeweler's magnifying goggles and leans over for a closer look, spraying the raw tattoo with a disinfectant/blood-wipe. The tattoo artists wear surgical gloves. Their tattoo needles are "glitter engraved." In the other chair a nice looking girl in a tank top and cut off jeans is having a lizard tattooed on the inside of her thigh. She sucks on a tootsie pop, staring up at the ceiling, trying to look brave as the needle eats the lizard into her skin.

The baddest looking bikers in Gunner's Lounge are members of the "Bandidos." Older guys from mean states—Texas, Oklahoma, Arkansas. An age when they've got nothing left to lose and nothing much to gain from life. One guy with a burn scar on the side of his face and his back patched and quilted with scars and skin grafts from, I assume, skidding down the highway in a motorcycle wreck. A necklace of skulls tattooed around his neck. A limp. Lots of guys with limps. Some still on crutches from more recent accidents. An occasional arm stub or amputated leg. One of the chapters has an aging thalidomide baby as a mascot, flippers where his arms and legs should be.

A color-pulsing jukebox plays a Willie Nelson/Johnny Cash/Kris Kristofferson song "I was a highwayman. . . . "

Video games flashing current top scores: "The records of the bravest fighters of Arkanoid."

A "No Fat Girls" sign behind the bar, but the huge young bartender with a babyface *looks* like a fat girl.

Guy with a leather top hat and Indian beaded band around it—like a mountain man. Leather straps on his arms.

Everybody smokes cigarettes.

"SONS OF SILENCE MC–IOWA."

Speed-freak girl. Absolutely emaciated with bad teeth—like a death camp survivor. Wearing boots, jeans and a tank top.

"EAT MORE PUSSY" T-shirt.

"Sweater Bumpers," non-pierced rings on girl's nipples. Also pierced nipples. One girl looking down at the indentation of her pierced nipple through her sweater tells me, "When I got

77

mine four years ago nobody had them. Now you can't go to a party without seeing them everywhere." She tells me that she pierced her own nipples with a hypodermic needle, her "old man" cupping it and holding an ice cube to it.

The local girls and bar maids are bleached blond with too much eye shadow. Young. A little overweight. Chain smoking cigarettes.

Lots of the women are, well, ugly. Fat. Worn out. Drug-wasted. Some of them with little tits but flaunting them. One big woman with big, though aging, tits. Flashes them.

Little dwarf crippled guy with a big scar across his forehead, getting drunk on double tequilas & beer chasers. "Keep on drinkin' those and we'll have to pour you out of the place," the bartender says.

A tall shaved head guy who works in the bar. Wearing all black and carrying a big flashlight. His T-shirt says, "IF YOU DON'T SPEAK ENGLISH GET THE FUCK OUT."

"What's the flashlight for?" one of the bikers asks him, looking at his buddies, smart-ass.

"Case the lights go off. An' to keep down vie-lance."

The "No Sambos" sign on the wall—a cartoon black man with exaggerated Negro features, a red circle and slash stamped on his face.

Bouncers sitting on stools inside the doors.

"Beyond Bitch. WAY Beyond." T-shirt on a girl.

I sleep in the back seat of the rental car that night, a few blocks off Main Street, and all night I hear the roar of bikes. I get to bed at three, and at 6 A.M. the brutal South Dakota August sun booms up over the hills.

Malcolm Forbes' green and gold jetliner low-leveling over Sturgis on Friday morning. He also has 80 motorcycles, the local paper says, including a green and gold Harley to match his jet. But he's just a "regular guy," the article says.

THE WALL OF DEATH: It's a traveling show from Florida, "The California Hell Riders Cycle Trick Show." The show I remember seeing as a kid at the county fair. I didn't think anyone was still doing it. A knock-down transportable wooden-slat two-story circular wall with a striped tent over the top. You take the stairs to a walkway at the top where you can look down into the pit which slopes slightly upward from a concave bottom. There is a steel cable strung around the top edge of the pit to keep the motorcycles from flying up and over the lip of the pit. The motorcycles start going around at the slightly sloped bottom, then, through centrifugal force, zoom round and round the circular walls. A sexy, sleazy-but-vulnerable girl taking tickets in a little booth at the foot of the stairs. She's not really pretty. Her complexion is bad and her figure unremarkable, but she's charming as she acts tough, squinting through the smoke from the cigarette in her mouth. And a wonderful announcer:

"The wall of death. It's all happening inside! High speed motorcycle thrills and chills!

"Free-hand trick and fancy acrobatic riding. Dips and dives of death. The finest in motorcycle entertainment. We're here to thrill and entertain you. If you're not satisfied, come on down and see the lady at the ticket booth and she'll give you your two dollars back—no questions asked.

"We feature American made machinery—defying all the laws of gravity, featuring the Australian pursuit race. See the lady in the ticket booth and find the place of your choice—topside.

"The ever-dangerous dips and dives of death—without the use of handlebars or controls. High speed motorcycle enter-tainment at its finest.

"Last call. They're giving the safety warnings on the inside. When the line ends, the show begins. Choice locations on topside. You don't have to run—you just have to hurry a little bit."

The catwalk is jammed with funky bikers and women with tattooed tits. These are not people who are easily impressed by motorcycle tricks. But since it was only two bucks, they thought they'd take a look. There's a smell of gasoline and greasy food and cigarette smoke beneath the tent roof as the bikers and their women talk and laugh.

Down below, the barker and a 20 year old kid stoop through the little entrance to the pit and fit a wooden door into it so that the bottom of the pit is completely enclosed. The floor of the pit is dirt and dead South Dakota grass stained with oil.

"I have two requests of you," the announcer says, looking up at the gallery, "Stand away from the wall for your own safety. And please, do not set your drinks on the edge of the wall."

He looks around the circle of faces above him—quite fearlessly, considering the type of audience he has, making eye contact. "Okay then, enjoy the show."

The kid starts up his Indian and begins to spiral up the center line painted around the middle section of the wall, the whole structure shuddering as he picks up speed, going around the center line, horizontal to the ground.

"Okay, fine, that's pretty neat, but. . . . " the crowd thinks.

Then he starts arcing up toward the lip of the pit, shallow arcs at first, then steeper and faster and closer to the cable stretched around the edge, the structure rocking at the top of each arc until he comes so close to the cable that people step back, worried that he'll flip over the edge and hit them. It's crazy! The kid slows down a little and the crowd cheers and applauds. These rough bikers take their arms from around their girl friends, stick their cigarettes in their mouths, and applaud, the tattoos on their shoulders and biceps flexing as they clap.

The announcer says something, then–

The kid picks up speed again, the round and eerr-round roar of the bike, the walls shuddering, and begins to arc again, higher and sharper than before, but now he's moving on the bike seat, his hands off the handlebars, waving to the crowd, then he slips one leg over the gas tank and rides sidesaddle, his arms in the air. He pivots both legs over to the other side. God damn! the crowd is going batshit. They hold dollar bills over the edge of the cable as he zooms up and back, climbing and diving, snatching the bills out of their hands. Strangers in the crowd look at each other, grinning and shaking their heads.

"You want to keep that beer away from the edge?" the announcer shouts over the PA system, pointing to some drunk, big but not-too-tough looking guy, and the people around him glare at him–"You fuck." "Get the fuck back." A long haired, ZZ Top-bearded guy in Bandido colors grabs the beer and throws it over his shoulder out of the tent. When the bills are all snatched, the kid coasts back to the ground.

The barker announces the "Australian Pursuit Race." He and the kid crank up the go-cart at the bottom of the pit, he gets in it and the kid pushes it up the slope of the wall as it sputters and putts and begins to circle. The engine dies and it coasts back down to the bottom.

They make adjustments on the go-cart engine. It sputters, coughs, then catches and spirals up to the center line where the driver, *sideways,* remember, drones and drones around, straddling the center line.

The kid cranks up the Indian and catches up with the go-cart, cruising behind it parallel to the ground, for a circuit or two, then he kicks it and goes over the top of the go-cart, and begins arcing up and down behind and in front of the go-cart, running vertical circles around the go-cart, coming within inches of the go-cart and then the cable with each arc. By now we adore the bravery of the kid and almost want him to stop. But he keeps arcing up and down, behind and over and down past the nose of the go-cart, effortlessly, missing it by inches as the crowd goes wild once again.

And then it's over. The announcer thanks the crowd as they begin to go down the stairs.

But there's another line waiting for their two dollar tickets and the dark haired, cheap, beautiful woman is selling tickets to the next show, smoking a cigarette and collecting dollar bills. This show goes on and on.

Bike drag races across the campground throw up dust. Sled pulls, bikes ripping their guts out pulling the concrete-weighted sheet-metal sleds. The tattooed biker woman in a bikini, taunting guys who are throwing baseballs trying to dunk her in a tank of water. The hammer bell-ring *dongs,* a biker swinging the big wooden-mallet hammer. Biker girls and women and biker crones flash their tattooed and nipple-pierced tits. The thunder clouds have passed over and the sun is going down, dust sparkling like mica in the sunset.

"It's all happening inside. High speed motorcycle thrills and chills. . . . "

The next day, on impulse, I stop at the Black Hills National Cemetery, one off-ramp before the exit to Sturgis. In fact, I pass the cemetery exit where the rows of white marble slabs, thousands of them, follow the contours of the rolling hills, then turn around in Sturgis and go back.

I park in front of the little administration building and go inside, through the first door, the foyer (it gets cold here in the winter) and the inside door. The little bell on the door rings and the two old-lady volunteers look up from behind their reception counter, happy to see a visitor, a "young man," though I'm hardly that any more. I'm real polite, grateful to them for working in this lonely place, taking care of the dead. That's how it is, I see now. Dead soldiers, when all the cursing and tears and military bands are over, when their wives have remarried and their children have forgotten them, the dead soldiers will be tended through the decades by old ladies like this. They press some brochures on me and I go out to walk among the graves.

The most prominent stone, facing the administration building, is that of a Medal of Honor winner:

Charles
Windolph
Medal of Honor
Sgt
US Army
Indian Wars
Dec 9 1851 - Mar 11 1950

"Indian Wars," I think. I walk among the graves. Way off in the distance three people are laying flowers. I see graves from the Spanish American War. Another:

Jacob Oscar Fenton
Cook
61 Balloon Company
Air Service
WW1

Then I come to a section marked in one corner by a brass plaque not much bigger than a postcard:

THE MARKERS IN THIS MEMORIAL AREA HONOR VETERANS WHOSE REMAINS HAVE NOT BEEN RECOVERED OR IDENTIFIED, WERE BURIED AT SEA, OR CREMATED AND THE ASHES SCATTERED.

These guys were all killed in battle. Every tombstone has the initials PH at the bottom—Purple Heart. They are almost all young, 20, 21, 22 years old. I see the grave of a 22 year old Major. I see:

James Marcelle La Pointe
Cox USN
WW II
July 15 1924 - April 16 1945
SS 2PH

A Silver Star and two Purple Hearts. How did he die, I wonder. In a gun tub in the Pacific firing at Kamikazes, his ship blown out for under him, lost at sea? Or steering a landing craft onto some beach-head in Europe, bodies floating in the surf, water geysering up around him until an 88 round blew up his craft and all the men in it. The dead never recovered, the bodies and pieces of bodies eaten by fish or bulldozed into mass graves off the beach.

I see that most of the Navy officers are "Lt (JG)"—Lieutenant, Junior Grade. Only Junior Grade, not full Lieutenants, mind you. They never lived long enough to make full Lieutenants. They want you to know they were not full Lieutenants.

And they all died in vain of course. They always will. All that stuff about Freedom and America is just, as James Jones said, "beautiful bullshit." Still, though, there is something here. I won't use the word honor, but most of these young men died doing their jobs in spite of the terror that tried to paralyze them. They kept marching, or steering, or shooting even as the smoke rolled over them and tore them to shreds. Dumb kids. What else could they do? They were only Junior Grade.

I realize that I am weeping, crying silently as I walk slowly across the grass, the empty graves of dead soldiers.

The thing about the sky in South Dakota is that it is so big. There may be thunderheads and rain in the east, while the sun shines in the west. It's as if it's the sky for the whole waking world, fading off at the edges into the darkness of the sleeping world. Little white flowers, tiny morning glories, thread through the grass among the tombstones, and I take care not to step on any of them.

That night I stop at the Elk Creek Steak House and Lounge for supper. I have a beer in the lounge and listen to a C&W band, young kids having a good time with the music. They cover the Randy Travis song that goes, "My love is deeper than the holler, stronger than the river, higher than the pine trees standing tall upon the hill. . . . " Though it is a happy song, it breaks my heart. The kids in the band will eventually give up their music, spend their lives as mechanics, 7-11 clerks, drunks, wife-beaters, convicts. Maybe, I think as they play, ". . . and soft as the *song*. . . of the whip-poor-will. . . ," it might be better if we had all died in one of those wars.

• • •

The Sturgis airport where—Plan B—I'm supposed to meet the San Fernando Valley chapter of the Hell's Angels, is a concrete block building with cheap paneled walls, like a waiting room at Midas Muffler. Copies of *South Dakota* magazines on a cigarette-burned coffee table headline topics like "Bee Stings," "Canning Wild Game," and "Rural Singles." I look *that* one up, but the pages have been torn out. The airport guy asks me, "You goin' to watch the ants?" (the hordes of bikers down in Sturgis).

"This is a real nice terminal," he says, looking out the window at the blacktop airstrip and the dayglow orange windsock, erect in the already hot morning wind. "One of the nicest in the state."

A dozen bikes roar past on highway 85. Eighty miles north, between Cow Butte and Mud Butte is the "Geographical

Center of the U.S. Still looking out the window, he says, "Most of them bikers are good people, just like you and me. It's just a few rotten apples cause the trouble. 'Course, as many as they got down here, it's gonna be a *lot* of rotten apples."

It smells of sweet, mown alfalfa outside, but it's empty, flat, hills way in the distance. Aside from passing bikes and the distant buzz of the town itself, it's so quiet it's spooky. I listen to my ears ring and chirp in the silence between bikes and think, "All they have here is summer and winter. Why would anyone stay?" I imagine snow blowing across the plains.

Freddy drives the van that picks me up. He's not a Hell's Angel, but is an "associate" member. He says he couldn't belong as a full member because he couldn't like a hundred motherfuckers enough to fight for all of them. That's the deal with the Angels and with most "outlaw" clubs. You fight one, you have to fight them all.

Freddy's done time in prison, I hear later, from one of the Angels—two stretches, "for killing two niggers." He's the most likable guy of the bunch, big and beer-bellied, a lot of muscle beneath the fat. His arms and chest are covered with jailhouse tattoos that are well done, not at all crude. I ask him how they did such *nice* work in prison.

"An eight track tape motor and a piece of E string from an electric guitar." The tape motor, he explains, has an eccentric flywheel that vibrates. They attach the stub of steel E string to the motor, then dip it in ball point pen ink. It works just like an electric tattoo needle.

On the way into town he tells stories, trying to shock me. "I have a terrible time keeping girl friends. This last one I had, I took her to a swap meet and a Doberman bit her face off. I had to find a new one." He sings, "You broke my heart so I broke your jaw. . . . " But Freddy's no dope, he sees that I'm not what they were expecting out of Hollywood, and soon we're talking more or less normally.

I meet six or eight other members having breakfast in town, including the president of the chapter, a relatively suave dude, six foot four or five, with clean shoulder length hair. His girlfriend is five foot at most, a tough cookie built like a gymnast, and I like her.

After introductions we leave the restaurant for a morning beer and things get off to a rocky start.

I'm walking behind the Prez and his girlfriend, taking pictures with my little point-and-shoot camera. I take a couple of the Prez in his Angel Colors and the other Angels guffaw. One of them says something to him and he turns, sees me with my camera, and walks up to me. He takes my left hand in both of his, examines it, asks me, "Is this one of the hands you type with?" I'm not sure what the problem is, but I *do* understand that he's threatening to break my hand.

I look him in the eyes and say, "Yeah." He still holds my hand, but we ignore it and talk with our eyes. My eyes say "fuck you," and I think about jumping on him and taking the beating I know I'll take from all of them. It'll put me in the hospital and fuck up any chance of the movie getting made, but that's what I should do. *Nobody's* threatened me like that for twenty years.

He drops my hand, without breaking eye contact, and tells me that the Angels don't want people taking their photograph when they're wearing their colors.

I tell him I didn't know that.

He says, OK, and goes back to his girlfriend.

When we get to Gunner's Lounge the Angels take a table and I go to the bar by myself to get a beer. But the Prez calls me over to the table where he tells one of the Angels to give me his chair, and buys me a beer.

87

It was two or three years before I realized that I had done exactly the right thing. The Prez, like Freddy and unlike many of the Angels, wasn't a dope. He knew I wasn't afraid of him, maybe even that I had been thinking about jumping on him. It would have been stupid of me to take that beating I'd considered.

Ironically, it seems like even the roughest looking biker has a little camera, to take pictures of tits. "Show your tits!" they yell. Whenever I'd see a cluster of bikers with flashing Insta-matics, I knew some girl was baring her breasts.

Bubba, one of the Angels, goes to a nearby booth for a Coke. He's tattooed, barechested, beer-bellied, a knife at his belt. "Gimme a Coke," he says. The kid picks up a regular coke and Bubba says, "A *diet* Coke. I don't need the sugar, man."

Walking down the street to buy more film, I see Christian Bikers—"Christian Motorcycle Association—Riding for the Son." Reformed drug addicts—"Fifth Chapter—Life After Drugs." I pass an AA chapter, "Friends of Bill W." painted over the door. Its big parking lot is filled with bikes, and bikers are lined up on the boardwalk, waiting to get into a meeting.

You can barely move through the crowd, but everyone is patient and polite. It's not a place you'd want to start a fight because it would turn into a *serious* fight right away. They wear boots and chains and knives. You couldn't bluff many of these guys, or make them back down. Working class and white trash, like me, they've *been* in fights, or in prison where you're finished once you back down, and will probably get fucked in the ass. I try not to make my usual eye contact with people on the street. Usually, except for those days I want to hide in the closet and whimper, I regard myself as the toughest guy on the street. Not here.

People leave their belongings on the seats of their bikes. A thief would get harsh treatment here. The kind of justice you find in prison or on the frontier, swift and hard, the way it should be.

• • •

Joe and Buddy come back from a visit to the titty bar at the end of the campground and describe the two naked women who oiled each other up and humped on the raised stage in the middle of the floor.

The "Buffalo Chip Campground" is bleak, sunbaked, and dusty, like one of those desert prison camps right-wing anti-crime people propose, surrounded by barbed wire and land mines. A few bikers criss-cross the hill out beyond the main stage, a hot breeze blowing the dust they kick up. Signs for TATTOOS–BEER–TACOS. A hand-lettered sign for "Bondage Items." Giant inflated "Purple Passion" bottles shudder in the heat.

I walk to the titty bar, hoping to see the oil wrestling, but it's all over. A crowd is growing outside the bar, surrounding a biker who's fucking a drunk Indian woman, standing up. Bare-breasted women stalk and stumble through the crowd, drunk or stoned, eyes like zombies. A hefty woman, her pierced nipples connected by a length of chain, stops to kiss several men before I lose sight of her. A lot of the women, many of them young and pretty, others older, getting heavy, wear leather-slut outfits, chain-link bras, crotchless chaps, and I'll admit it, they're pretty erotic. Hank Williams, Jr. is on the jukebox back in the plywood-walled bar singing "Family Affair," and the crowed sings along. It's like a Brueghel painting, I think, come to life here. A biker sitting on one of the picnic tables has a woman in his lap. He pulls up her blouse and begins to lick and suck her tits.

89

The fine, blown dust collects in my eyes and nose, on my sunburned cheekbones and neck.

The Indian woman is giving another guy a blow job. The crowd around them reminds me of spectators at a fatal traffic accident. The same look in their eyes. Some of them are edging in closer with their Instamatics to their eyes. The Indian woman sits in the lap of one biker who straddles a Harley "Fat Boy." He plays with her tits while she laughs weirdly, wearing dark granny glasses that make her look blind. Another biker pulls out his dick, and the one on the motorcycle pushes the laughing woman's face down onto it. "Come on," the biker says as she goes down on him, "do it like you *mean* it." A stocky Indian in a leather vest, her pimp, watches impassively.

Back out on the camp grounds I stop to watch a drunk woman unstrap her leather halter top so bikers can take photos of her tits. She leans back and thrusts out her chest, "Come on then, you fuckers, this is your chance." Then pulls a waterpistol out of the waistband of her leather mini-skirt and holds it up between her tits, a realistic, blue-veined penis squirt gun.

A man and woman walk past the Easy Rider tent. She's wearing black leather too, a push-up halter top with vertical zippers down each breast. Somebody yells, "Show your tits!" She peels the top down, her man beaming with pride of ownership. He steps behind her, cups her breasts and squeezes them together for the cameras. It looks like it must hurt. One of the guys taking photos says, "I want you to know, this lady grabbed my attention right away." And another, to her, "you stand out like a sore thumb."

A tiny little woman in a pink bikini does gymnast-like contortions on the motorcycle that ABATE is selling raffle tickets for. She looks about 16, with a great body and an okay face, but she has a frozen smile that makes her look psychotic or retarded. She takes off her top, cups her breasts and licks them, then bites her nipples, all the while looking out at the crowd with that scary smile. The ABATE guy next to her talks into a squealing mike: "All right. You can win this bike *or* the girl. The more tickets you buy, the better chance you have. . . . " The girl takes off her pants and does gymnast contortions on the leather motorcycle seat.

I walk away for a beer and see the woman in the push-up halter top shopping one of the T-shirt booths, her leather bra cups unzipped, nipples sticking out.

I see the little woman in the pink bikini again, at a booth where they are going to "auction her off," as soon as they finish the "chicken shit contest." Four chickens walk around in a wire cage, the plywood floor marked off in numbered grids. One of the chickens shits, and the biker who bet on the grid it hits wins 25 dollars. This booth is run by women. The announcer is big and chunky, middle-aged, with bright purple hair. "Now we're gonna auction off this little girl. She comes with a certificate for two prime rib dinners at Costanzo's Restaurant, the best prime rib in the state. She's gonna look good on the back of somebody's Harley."

The girl goes into contortions, pantomiming "Fuck me,"or "Look at *this,*" and I wonder if she's deaf & dumb.

"It's all in fun and for a good cause, the Rapid City Battered Women's Shelter."

"God knows there's enough of *those,*" a second woman says.

"She *is* eighteen. I know she looks younger, but she's not jailbait." She never uses the girl's name, the girl never speaks. "We're just auctioning off a date for dinner. Whatever you do after that is your business."

She starts off the bidding with a thousand dollars, and the crowd laughs. She drops to a hundred dollars. No bids. The girl pulls down her top and bites her nipples, never taking her eyes off the crowd.

They drop the opening bid to twenty-five dollars. "If we can't get twenty-five, fuck it. It ain't worth it. The dinner alone is worth twenty-five." A guy videotaping from the top of a van raises his hand to bid twenty-five.

"Okay. We've got twenty-five. Do I hear thirty-five?" The girl pulls off her top and does the splits on her platform, pumping her crotch up and down. She cups her ear toward the crowd, miming that she is listening for a bid. The guy on top of the van tops his own bid to thirty.

"Come on, do I hear fifty? It's for the Rapid City Battered Women's Shelter." No bids. The girl raises halfway up from her split, and the second woman hooks a finger in the girl's bikini bottom, pulling it down so we can see her pubic hair.

"Come on. Look at that. What else could you want? Who'll bid fifty?" The guy on the van bids fifty. Finally they get the bid up to a hundred dollars, but as far as I can see, the guy on the van is the only person bidding–against himself.

• • •

I'd seen him in the titty bar. A relatively thin, unmuscular dude compared to the buffed out, beer-bellied, or wiry bikers. Now that the bands have started playing, he's wearing red, one-piece long johns and a mask made from a piece of black cloth with eye-holes torn in it. He struts and dances through the crowd, unbuttoning the rear flap of the long johns to show polka dot underwear. He's up in front of the stage, the crotch of the long johns unbuttoned, polka dot underwear hanging over the front like a codpiece. He pulls the underwear aside and flashes his dick.

I figure he's done prison time and was a punk, a homosexual "girl" in there, misses it, and is looking to get butt-fucked before the night is over.

Another band comes on stage. It's three in the afternoon, and the sun beats down on the crowd. The band's name is Little Caesar, from LA. A working-class heavy metal band. The barechested lead singer has waist length black hair. Intricate tattoos cover his arms, shoulders, and back. He's wiry, about 25, and as he sings he stalks across the stage, throwing his hair like a Kabuki dancer, leaping, spinning, putting out enormous energy.

"We're from LA, and yeah, I know that's a drag. Nobody gives a shit for anybody but themselves down there . . . but if we stick together, we can show the *assholes* a few things. All we need is our honor. We've got our own law here. We're *family.* Where else can you just leave your shit laying on the ground and know that nobody is gonna fuck with it? We don't have to take shit from *nobody.*"

The audience, out in the sun, raise their clenched fists. Some of them have bandages on their arms, covering fresh tattoos, some wear casts on broken arms and legs, beards, silver studded leather, sunglasses flashing in the sun. Cigarette smoke rises from the crowd, mixing with dust in the hot breeze. Flags fly from tents and on the backs of motorcycles on the hill behind the crowd—American flags, Texas, Rebels, POW flags. A heavy timber and chainlink fence separates the audience from the front of the stage, and people hang on it, looking up at the band, like inmates at a concentration camp. After their last number, the singer yells, "Don't take shit from *nobody!*"

They leave the stage, staggering from the heat and exhaustion, while the crowd cheers.

I go find a beer and something to eat, a BBQ beef sandwich, thick slabs of tasteless meat in an industrial-strength BBQ sauce. Catsup meat. It gives me food poisoning.

Barely able to walk the next day. Eating at "Perkin's Family Restaurant." Muzac and tablecloths and blue-haired old ladies and *nice* families—feeling dizzy and spaced-out and paranoid, out of place there, trying not to attract attention to myself, trying to be invisible. If Sturgis is the moon, I think, and Hollywood is Mars, the Rapid City Perkins Family Restaurant Sunday Brunch is Jupiter.

SHANK
(1990-91)

There Are A Couple spots
in Here that Might Be
slightly Confusing — But I
Figured they'd Be Clarified
During the Filming — Haz Haz —

Ken

BLACK SCREEN

We HEAR a tinny old rock song, the worn tape slightly distorted. It sounds like failures and lost dreams.

FADE IN:

INT.–HARPO'S TOPLESS-PLUS–NIGHT

A seedy working class bar, smoky and hot. Too dark to make out individual faces. A topless dancer appears almost to float in the dark on a little suspended stage. Pasty white and not especially pretty, she goes through the motions under a glaring spotlight, dancing listlessly to the music that opens the movie.
At the bar, where the anonymous drinkers pay little attention to the dancer, we hear the CRASH of breaking glass.

> BARTENDER
> Time to go home, pal. A man should know his limits. You ever think about that?

One of the drinkers detaches from the crowd.

> BARTENDER
> *Help* the man out, Marco.

A bouncer looms out of the darkness and takes the drunk by the arm. But when the drunk looks up at him he lets go and takes half a step back.

EXT.– HARPO'S–NIGHT

Beneath the half-burned-out neon sign, we watch through the door as the drunk staggers toward us. The bar is dimly lit, but is brighter than the darkness outside.

> BARTENDER (OS)
> I said, *help* him out.

> MARCO (OS)
> He's *out,* OK?

The drunk makes it across the parking lot and leans against the hood of his pickup. He straightens up, takes a couple of breaths, then suddenly bends over as if he's going to be sick. Nothing. He reaches into the truck to open the broken door from the inside, then turns and *does* throw up just as the moon breaks through the clouds for a few seconds, making broken glass littering the lot glitter like stars.

CLOSE: HIS FACE

As he looks up at the moon. It's CAP, a good man who's been beat up so much by life that, as tough and brave as he is, he's just about done for.
The clouds close back up as he gets in the battered truck, starts it on the second try, and drives out of the lot bumping over the curb and onto a divided four-lane street.
It's Sunday night and the street is almost deserted.

CLOSE: THE TRUCK'S RADIO

The faint light from the dial illuminates Cap's scarred hand as he turns the dial, going from static to static. Then he gets a faint sweet song.
This is "Cap's song," and we'll hear it again, a song full of memories. It fades out and he tries to find it again. Nothing. He SLAMS his hand against the radio and the truck lurches across the center line. He turns the dial and gets another station, an urgent whisper that he can't coax louder.

He leans over to turn on the headlights and WE see the Oakland Police car in the rear view mirror. Cap HITS the radio, the truck lurching again, then HE sees the patrol car.

The reflection of overhead streetlights slides over the hood and up the windshield of the patrol car like prison bars, like the slow passage of hard time. One of the cops is on the radio, obviously running the truck's plate.

CLOSE: the dusty speedometer as the needle twitches above and below 35 as Cap tries to keep his speed steady. He turns off the four-lane onto a narrow neighborhood street. In the CRACKED SIDE VIEW MIRROR we see the splintered image of the patrol car following.

The whisper on the radio suddenly BLARES through the cracked speaker—a DJ on a Mexican station. Mad, rabid Spanish. Cap twists the volume, the on/off, punches the preset buttons but the voice blares on, unstoppable, as the red and blue police lights swarm through the cab of the truck. Cap downshifts, pulling to the curb, as we hear a squealing of tires behind him and the lights flare crazily and begin to fade as the PATROL CAR fishtails then stablizes, accelerating AWAY, down the street to the intersection where it hesitates, flips on the siren, and peels down the street and out of sight, siren wailing, on the way to some emergency. A moment later we hear sirens, and a second patrol car, then a *third* flashes code-3 through the intersection after the first. Cap hits the curb where the transmission bucks, killing the engine and the raving DJ.

He looks at the floorboard on the passenger side of the cab, as if trying to remember something, then reaches down and digs through beer cans and Big Mac boxes, searching for something. We know by the look on his face when he finds it.

He pulls out a plastic Jesus, rubs it on his shirt, cleaning it off as best he can, then holds it up to the dim light. It's cracked and dirty, pale as the dancer in Harpo's bar.

CAP (slight Southern accent)
Thank you Jeezus. You can ride up here with me.

He knocks some junk off the dashboard and lays the Jesus in a dent next to a Harley Davidson decal, then slumps in the seat, breathing sweet air in the wonderful radio silence. He speaks slowly at first, recalling long forgotten words, then his rap builds, gathers authority and rhythm, words burned into him as a fundamentalist minister's son.

CAP
Thank Jeezus. I been *chosen.* And the *chosen* now, if
you been chosen you can walk through the fire and
take up snakes and serpents in your hands.

Laughing, but still rapping, he starts the engine and the RADIO shatters the silence. Cap drives off, shouting against the raving Mexican DJ.

CAP
You can talk in tongues, people. Take up serpents
and *command* them, in Jeezus' name, to harm you
not, if you are the chosen. . . .

EXT.–CAP'S HOUSE–NIGHT

Two young gang kids sit on the steps smoking crack. They laugh as Cap bounces the truck off the curb and kills the engine. He stops in the yard, puzzled, looking at a new "For Rent" sign. Down the street behind him, a faint green glow fills the windshield of a battered VAN, then fades away.

KID #1
My man. Fucked up *again.* That booze gonna kill
you.

99

In the flare of his lighter the kid looks like a little demon as he inhales.

                    KID #2
    Fuck that booze. You need to do some *crack*, my
    man. Crack–bring you *back.*

                     CAP
    I need to do some sleep.

QUICK CUT TO:

Starlight scope POV from down the street. Cap's house, the glowing crack pipe bright as a porch light.

CUT BACK TO:

                   KID #1
    Shit! We'll sleep when we be dead.

They laugh as Cap notices the lock cut off the security door.

                   KID #1
    A moving van, big Bekin's van took it away. *We*
    didn't take your shit.

                   KID #2
    None of it worth anything. (standing up to #1)
    Come on, boy. Let's check out the night.

                   Kid #1
    Do or die.

They walk away laughing. The door has been wired shut, and Cap fumbles drunkenly with the wire.

CUT TO:

The green night-vision scope POV of Cap.

> CAP (electronic VO)
> A little *light* might help.

The view through the scope FLARES into green static as the spotlight over the door scrambles the scope's circuitry.

> WHITEY (OS)
> Goddamn equipment. The ad said it was *reconditioned.*

INT.–CAP'S HOUSE–NIGHT

He turns on the wall switch and a single dim light comes on. The wall separating living room from kitchen was knocked out long ago. The place is empty. All that remains of the furniture are outlines on the filthy carpet.

In the kitchen, the huge old refrigerator is unplugged, in the middle of the floor, too big to get through the door. A legal notice is taped to the refrigerator, a handwritten note and a twenty-dollar bill beneath it. Cap peels the note off the door and begins to read when the lightbulb burns out with a blue flash and Cap tries but fails to read by starlight coming through a dirty window. The refrigerator glows dirty white, massive. Cap tries to plug it in, but the cord won't reach.

INT.–VAN–NIGHT

> CAP (OS) (filtered through the directional mike)
> Grunting and panting.

> DUKE
> Listen! He's got a woman in there. *That's* why he turned out the light. . . .

INT.–HOUSE–NIGHT

Out of breath, Cap wrestles the refrigerator to the wall and plugs it in. He opens the door and reads the note by the stale light inside, pushing aside spoiled food and a single can of beer.

                    NOTE
          Cap–Our attorney says the divorce might be
          invalid if you stay in the house with custody of joint
          property. I insisted they leave your bike, knowing
          how much it means to you. Please be out of the
          house by Wednesday. I'm sorry.
                                        – Nancy.

          A junk dealer gave us $20.00 for the lot. You keep
          it.

Cap jams the money in his pocket, rips the beer open on his way to the stairs, and half of it spews out. Something gleams faintly on the floor and he picks it up. A picture frame.

INT.–VAN–NIGHT

Whitey, Pogo and Duke, dressed in black fatigues, pull on black ski masks and feel around for equipment–guns, walkie-talkies, flashlights, army surplus stuff–stumbling over each other in the dark van.

                    POGO
          These fuckin' masks are *hot,* man. . . .

                    WHITEY
          Shut up, if . . . don't *point* that gun at me. I'll stick it
          up your ass. Damn. Rule number *one,* always keep
          the muzzle. . . .

DUKE

My walkie talkie doesn't work. The little red light
won't even come on.

WHITEY

Checklist, man, checklist. Transceiver failure.
Primary cause? Think!

DUKE

Shit. I must of forgot to turn it off last night. Where's
the batteries?

POGO

Don't ask me. *You* were supposed to buy
some more. . . .

INT.–HOUSE–NIGHT

The small, windowless second floor room has been stripped of
everything but the beautifully rebuilt Harley and a gas can. The
door to the room is the only solid thing in the house, squares of
sheet-steel bolted to the outside, a police-lock on the inside. A
locksmith's business card is stuck in the lock.

EXT.–STREET–NIGHT

Whitey, Pogo and Duke cross the street one after the other, then
work their way along a fence two houses down. Whitey's hand
and arm signals are mostly ignored by the other two. Whitey carries
an MP5, Duke has a folding stock Benelli shotgun, and Pogo has a
MAC 10 with suppressor–"Hi-tech," mostly foreign-made stuff that
will contrast with the beat-up weapons the bikers will carry. These
guys got their moves from *Soldier of Fortune,* instructional tapes,
and TV. They are inept, but vicious, like brain-damaged Dobermans. When a barking dog hits the fence, Duke's shotgun BOOMS.

INT.–HOUSE–NIGHT

Cap sits on the bike, looking at the framed photo of Cap, Shank, and Willie, taken maybe twelve years before when Willie was twelve or thirteen. Cap looks twenty years younger. Willie looks like a nerd. They stand in front of this same motorcycle, off on the shoulder of a curving road above the ocean that gleams like silver in the late afternoon sun. They're all smiling, squinting against the glare as the shadow of the photographer falls across them. Cap's head comes up at the sound of the dog and SHOTGUN, then he laughs and speaks to the photo.

CAP

Luther's still trying to house-train that dog of his.

INT.–HOUSE–NIGHT

Whitey, Pogo and Duke come through the door, then huddle behind the refrigerator. Pogo nervously tightens and loosens the suppressor on his MAC 10. Duke tries to close his hand on the pistol grip of the shotgun and winces.

DUKE (whispers)

Fuckin' gun like to broke my wrist.

WHITEY

Take the pain. Pogo, I *told* you. Don't fuck with the suppressor. You'll strip the threads. Have you got the mace?

Pogo slings his MAC 10 and pulls a jail-size can of mace out of a satchel.

POGO

Ten-four. That's affirmed. Hose his ass down with this, he won't know whether to shit or go blind. (giggles)

WHITEY
I'll take the point, utilizing the mirror to make a
visual search before we attempt room entry.

Whitey extends a car radio antenna, a convex sideview mirror
attached to the end, and they move toward the stairs.

INT.–ROOM–NIGHT

Cap hears something and glances at the door, then does a
double-take as a silver mirror floats into view, Whitey's face
distorted in the convex glass, looking at him. Cap looks back,
bewildered. Is he still *that* drunk? Then Pogo steps into the doorway, aiming the can of mace at him in some sort of "combat stance."
Nothing happens. While Pogo fumbles with a safety cap, Cap
SLAMS the door into him, latching it and setting the police lock
in a single motion as a shotgun BOOMS in the hallway.

INT.–HALLWAY–NIGHT

Pogo has maced himself and the others. He flings down the
still-spurting mace canister and struggles to pull off his smoking
wool ski mask, scorched by the muzzle flash of Duke's folding
stock shotgun. Whitey rakes the ceiling with automatic fire, enraged,
shouting orders, plaster dust drifting down onto them.

CUT TO:
CAP, looking for some way out as the shotgun hammers the door
and the HK splinters the threshold.

CUT TO:

The HALL–boiling with gunsmoke and strobing muzzle
blasts,Whitey and the others sweating, red-faced and half-blinded
by the mace. Pogo braces himself and his suppressed MAC 10
snarls, showering Whitey with hot expended brass, the full-jacketed

105

slugs ricocheting off the door. He puts in a new clip and when the loosened suppressor EXPLODES off the barrel he laughs madly and keeps firing, the weapon DEAFENING now.

CUT TO:

CAP. Coolly pouring gas into the tank, priming the fuel pump as the flimsy walls fall apart, bullets cracking past, only the door shielding him. He calmly kicks the starter. Again. He adjusts the choke, kicks it again, and the Harley roars into life. He smashes the picture frame on his boot, and pulls out the photo.

Behind him, the shotgun muzzle breaks through the sheetrock and blindly patterns the outside wall with buckshot. Cap tosses the gas can at the shotgun barrel, gasoline spooling from the mouth. He's SMILING, happier than he's been in a long time as he looks at the photo.

CAP

You and me, right kid?

When he tucks the photo into his shirt he feels something else there that makes him grin even more. A lighter. He strikes a flame while revving the Harley, holding the front brake with the other hand, the bike fishtailing madly.

CAP

Let's see 'em rent the fucker out now.

He throws the lighter over his shoulder, grips both handlebars and rises in a SHRIEKING wheelie, filling the frame as the gas FLARES behind him, filling the room with yellow light and he HITS THE WALL . . . sideways, splintering sheetrock and studs as they jerk him off the bike. He falls onto a hedge, watching the bike bounce once on its wheels, lay down in a shower of sparks, rebound, and race away. Above him, flames shoot out of the jagged

106

hole he came through, haloing it in fire for a moment before the roof collapses.

We ZOOM up, up, to where we see the flaming house far below, lighting the neighborhood, smoke rising, obscuring the lens, then FADE TO

EXT.–TINY'S JUNKYARD–NIGHT

Crushed cars and jagged stacks of scrap iron glow sullenly in the lights of the refinery complex looming just beyond it like the gateway to hell. White smoke boils under hundreds of floodlights and flames pulse out of burn-off tubes. A guard dog appears, then fades into the shadows as we move through dead cars toward the little office. The sign above it reads, "Tiny's Second Chance–U-Pic Junk," and beneath it, "World Headquarters–Tiny's smooth-the-road RV suspensions."

INT.–TINY'S "OFFICE"–NIGHT

The front room lined with bookcases, a bedroom and kitchenette in the back, spartan and spotless as a monk's quarters. Tiny reads by the green light from a banker's lamp. Light from the refinery flares like heat lightning beyond the barred windows.
Tiny is, of course, enormous, his long pointed beard giving him the look of an Old Testament prophet. Tattoos coil out at the wrists and collar of his long-sleeved coveralls, the only clothes he ever wears. He closes the book, looks at the door, waiting. At the knock, he gets up and opens it.
It's Cap, beat to shit, wrecked bike in the truck behind him.

                                    CAP
          Just a little accident. I'll live.

Tiny nods and looks out at the wrecked bike.

TINY

You told me you weren't going to put it on the street
till you got straight. What was it you said? "Something to keep me out of the bars." (beat) How'd
you get it out the door?

CAP

I didn't take it out the door. (beat) And I didn't put
it on the street, either. I said I wouldn't and I didn't.
I might be a drunk and a fuck-up, but I do what I
say I'll do, and if you doubt. . . .

He turns and walks to the truck, still talking.

. . . that, then I'm gone. Adios. Nobody, not even
you, calls me a liar.

TINY

Come in the house. Get some sleep. You must have
a concussion.

CAP

I do *not*. I'm fine. I've damn sure *had* enough
goddamned concussions in my life to *know* when
I've. . . .

INT.– TINY'S BED–NIGHT

Cap is passed out on the bed, his boots sticking out from the
lightning pattern quilt that covers him. Tiny, huge, FILLING THE
SCREEN, looks down at him.

TINY

That was hard time you did–when it was somebody
else should have done it. You never said anything,

108

and you think no one knows. There's two of us know it, bro. Sleep good.

Tiny walks OUT OF THE FRAME, no longer in our way, and we SEE the little photo on a bookshelf. Tiny, Shank, and Cap, silver trophies held aloft, smile out at us from years ago.

INT.–BEDROOM–DAY

Cap wakes up hungover, just as we hear a gasoline engine start up, race, then settle into a powerful purr (this has to be a very distinctive sound so we'll recognize it when we hear it again at the end of the movie).

INT.–TINY'S SHOP–DAY

It's as spotless as his house, gleaming grays and silvers, black iron and gunmetal blues, drill-presses, vices, welding equipment, hammers and wrenches on the walls, it looks like the god Vulcan's workshop. The gas engine we heard is bolted to a steel workbench. Cap shouts over the roar.

> CAP (sarcastic)
> You doing lawn mower repairs now?

> TINY
> Generator. Army surplus.

He plugs a thick electric cord into the motor housing and banks of fluorescent lights shudder and flash on, one by one across the ceiling, filling the shop with a strange light, illuminating a GLEAMING bundle of steel tubes, gearboxes and strangely shaped housings at the end of the workbench, the word VULCAN forged into the largest of them.

TINY

You can find just about anything in those Army-
Navy stores if you know what to look for.

CAP

Where's Shank?

Tiny shakes his head, tinkers with the engine.

CAP

You're the one person who'd know. Maybe if I
could talk to Shank. . . .

Tiny kills the engine and the strange hardware on the bench fades
into shadows as the lights go out. In the silence

TINY

He's out of it. Got a new life. Those days riding
with the Berserkers are gone. It's a different world
now.

EXT.–JUNKYARD–DAY

As they work without talking on the banged-up bike. Finally Tiny
has to ask. Neither of them look up from their work during the
conversation, Cap *wrenching* with increasing anger.

TINY

If you didn't put it on the street, then how. . . .

CAP

It happened in the house.

TINY

What do you *mean,* "it happened in the house?"

110

CAP

I rode it through a wall.

TINY

Man, I thought you were getting straight. You told
me you were off the *drugs* at. . . .

CAP

I *was* straight, dammit. Three motherfuckers
dressed like a SWAT team were shooting the damn
door down. I didn't have a whole lot of *selection*.

They work without talking, wrenching, grunting, the *clang* of a
dropped tool, then

TINY

Through the *wall?* You been watching Hollywood
biker movies? Those things are written by 25 year
old kids who dress like actors on *Miami Vice*.

CAP

I *told* you. I didn't have much choice.

Cap wrenches savagely at this, then, as he works, we can see his
anger fading.

CAP

Threw my ass through the sheetrock like a human
cannonball, tore out the studs and the whole damn
roof collapsed.

They keep working, then look up at each other and start to laugh.
The laughter builds to a roar as we

CUT TO:

INT.–TINY'S OFFICE–NIGHT

111

Cap is sitting on the floor, his back against Tiny's desk. Tiny, a book in his hands, watches from his chair, trying not to show his disapproval, as Cap drinks from another half-pint of vodka. He sets the bottle down and holds up the 20 dollar bill that was taped on the refrigerator.

                    CAP
        Tomorrow I'll give *this* back to my bitch ex-wife–
        she can *shove* it–then. . . .

                    TINY
        Nancy's a good woman. She never lied to
        you. When you took the rap for. . . .

Cap gives him a *look*.

                    TINY
        . . . rather than testify against another member of
        the Berserkers, what did you expect her to do?

                    CAP
        She could of. . . . Hell, why should I expect her to
        do anything? I'm just white trash from Mystic,
        Georgia. My daddy was a crazy preacher who
        talked in tongues and handled snakes on Sundays.
        It was her chance to get rid of me.

                    TINY
        She never complained. She had to make a living
        and raise your kid.

Cap calms down, thinks about it.

                    CAP
        He's real smart. Nothing like me. Still in that hot-shit
        college down in Palo Alto–Sanford, Stafford, what-

ever it is. He told Nancy he's gonna be a millionaire by the time he's thirty.

Tiny almost says something, then goes back his book.

                          CAP
What?

                          TINY
How many times did he come to see you?

                          CAP
He was just a kid. Nancy didn't want him in a place like that.

                          TINY
He hasn't been a kid for years. Nancy still telling him what to do?

                          CAP
I didn't want him to see me locked up like that.

                          TINY
What you wanted doesn't matter. It's what he should have *done.*

                    CAP (angry)
He didn't have anybody to *teach* him how to act. I wasn't there to do it. So it's on *me,* not him, how he turned out. Hell, he's probably better off. Read your goddamn book. . . .

Cap kills the bottle of vodka. Tiny goes back to his book, then looks at the photo on the bookshelf.

CLOSE:

113

The photo, in a silver frame. A dream-like black and white print. Tiny, Cap, and Shank, holding up silver trophies, faces dirty behind old-fashioned goggles, smiling out from years ago.

> TINY (OS)
> We respected you for what you did. The club began to fall apart after that. Shank and I walked away from it. You couldn't do that. (beat) The run to Sturgis is this week. Maybe you should go.

Cap is pretty wiped out now. He looks up at Tiny with blood-shot eyes.

> CAP
> Sturgis? Why? That's where all the backstabbing motherfuckers. . . .

> T I NY
> Remember how we made the run to Sturgis? Up through Redding and Portland to pick up the membership there. . . .

> CAP
> Redding. Always hotter than hell in August. The Gypsy Jokers in Portland would ride with us. Take Highway 12, uh, 97 miles to Walla Walla, a hundred and three more to Lewiston, then drop down Lolo Pass—remember that *green* river—to Missoula and drink some beer at the Eastgate. Through that pretty little piece of country east of Missoula. (beat) Shank always said he'd like to own some land there. . . .

> TINY
> You look like shit. Get some sleep.

INT.–TINY'S WORKSHOP–NIGHT

Tiny working on the generator with an arc welder. The light flashing blue on his facemask, tendrils of smoke rising like snakes.

EXT.– JUNKYARD–DAY

Tiny working on his three-wheeler bike. It has a Chevy 409 engine and a platform behind the seat. A retired couple pull up in a RV, American flag decals across the side, and the driver rolls down the window.

> DRIVER
>
> Thanks again, son. Those trips down to Winter-haven are a lot easier on an old man with that suspension you put in.

A blue-haired woman holds a miniature poodle out the window.

> WOMAN
>
> I bet you won't forget Petey, the dog that sings.

> TINY
>
> No, Ma'am.

> WOMAN
>
> Petey! Tell Tiny good-bye.

The dog barks. Tiny smiles, gives them a little wave, and watches them drive off. Cap rides up in his leathers, a swashbuckler again, and revs the Harley. It's thunderous, precisely tuned.

> CAP
>
> Good as new. Better. Thanks, Tiny. For taking care of my leathers, too.

They shake hands and time stops. For a moment we see the old Cap. There's a lot of history between these two, their bond of trust and respect undiminished by these troubled times.

CAP

I think I'll head out to Sturgis.

Tiny nods, is about to turn away, then

TINY

Who were they? Those three guys?

CAP

These days? Who knows? Coked-out survivalists, satanists, DEA agents with a bad address? Nobody I'll ever see again.

EXT.–PHONE BOOTH–DAY

Whitey is on the phone in a dirty and battered glass phone booth in an old industrial district. Duke leans in to listen, while Pogo squats at the edge of the road lobbing pebbles at a beer can. Whitey's hair is singed. Duke's eyebrows and eyelashes are gone, giving him a permanent "surprised" look. Pogo has a broken nose, black eyes, and a swollen lip that interferes with his speech. Whitey listens, his expression suggesting that someone is chewing him out. PULL BACK TO SHOW the entrance to TINY'S JUNK-YARD half a mile down the potholed road.

WHITEY

Yes sir. Absolutely. "Whatever it takes to accomplish the mission."

Whitey listens, nods. Pogo begins tossing pebbles at Duke, who ignores them as WE see Cap pull out of the junkyard and ride away. Pogo throws a small rock, *hard*. Duke spins around when it hits him in the neck and sees Cap pulling away. When he tugs at Whitey's arm, Whitey shoves him away.

116

WHITEY
You can count on us, sir. We've secured. . . .

Duke keeps tugging, hissing, nodding in the direction Cap has gone. Whitey finally covers the receiver with his hand.

WHITEY (into phone)
Excuse me a second, sir. (to Duke) What?

EXT.–GHOST TOWN–DAY

The sun HAMMERS a deserted mining town, the air roiling with rainbows of shimmering heat as we continue to hear Whitey. His voice is filtered through a phone, muffled by his hand.

WHITEY (CONT.OC)
Goddamit *what?* I'm talking to the deputy agent
in charge here and. . . .

As we notice *something* odd about the ghost town, the glint of hard-edged steel beams here and there. Whitey's voice, LOUD now, startles us as something FLASHES in the cruel blue sky way out over the horizon.

WHITEY (OC)
Sir?
VOICE (OC) (irritated)
Yes? I'm still here.

Now we can see that the FLASH is a helicopter, dropping down below the horizon. Just a silver speck against the desert floor. We can barely hear it, but it's coming this way as something very close to us throws a SHADOW across the frame.

WHITEY (OS)
Our subject is on the move, so I'll. . . .

117

VOICE (OC)

Stay with him. Go.

WHITEY (OC)

Roger that, sir, we. . . .

The phone BANGS, clatters, as if it was dropped, excited, quarrel-
ing voices in BG, as the helicopter gets closer and LOUDER, a
silver Huey with red, white and blue lettering. We hear the (OC)
WHINE of a dial tone as the POUNDING chopper fills the screen,
the words U.S. YANKEE AIR across the nose. The sound of the
chopper fades as it makes a wide circle to land at what we NOW
SEE is an airstrip.

The SHADOW deepens and a FACE fills the frame, a Peruvian
Indian, long black hair tied back in a bandanna. His face, ravaged
by some 3rd world childhood disease, is pitted with scars, part of
his nose gone. He looks at us, his eyes black and hard as stones.
The BG dial tone WHINE stops as we

CUT TO:

INT.–DEA OFFICE–DAY

Where Assistant Agent in Charge JAMES DURHAM hangs up
the phone. MCCOY, a compact man with close cropped hair, sits
on the edge of his desk, smiling. We see the silver chopper through
a window, landing in its own little sandstorm, as SOLDIERS run
toward it. They aren't American troops, but Peruvian "Panther
Brigade" Rangers, former terrorists for the *Sendero Luminoso*.
Durham, through the DEA, bought them out of prison and
requested Special Forces troops to train them. A private army,
much like the Chinese Nungs in Vietnam.

MCCOY (laughs)

Whitey, Pogo and *Duke*. 'Durham's dirty dozen'
minus nine.

DURHAM
How the hell am I supposed to fight a 'war on drugs' with scum like that? Our funding cut in half by Teddy Kennedy and the other do-good liberal *faggots*. . . .

McCoy's LAUGHTER builds as Durham reaches for the phone, a framed portrait of Richard M. Nixon on the wall behind him.

DURHAM
I *have* to cash in a few more kilos.

McCoy holds his hands over his ears, hops off the desk.

MCCOY
I didn't hear *that.* Time for a beer.

He throws a snappy salute at Nixon, and goes out the door.

MCCOY
Tricky Dickey.

EXT.–TELEGRAPH AVE.–DAY

It looks like we're back in the 60s, tie-dye and street musicians, political posters and graffiti, beads and granny glasses, a demonstration, angry speakers up the street. We HEAR (OC) faint piano music, tentative at first, uncertain, as CAP works his way through the traffic. He pulls away, and the music grows louder, surer. "Cap's song." The music continues as we
CUT TO:

INT.– NANCY'S HOUSE–DAY
A huge gated house in the Berkeley hills, with a view of the bay and San Francisco through the windows of the second floor room where Willie plays "Cap's song" on a grand piano, smiling, lost in

the music. A handsome, well-built young man in his early twenties, he plays very well, and we *like* him. He is thoughtful, earnest, his emotion building until the SOUND of the GRINDING electric gate opening in the courtyard below breaks the spell. Nancy and her second husband, Frank, drive up in a Mercedes 350 convertible. The qualities we liked in Willie's face are disappearing. He closes the keyboard, and when his mother enters the room he appears to be absorbed in a laptop computer on the coffee table.

NANCY

Still at it? This is your vacation.

WILLIE

It's the only way to stay number one.

FRANK

He's right. Number one in his class, the phone ringing off the hook with job offers from every. . . .

At this, Willie turns off the laptop, seething with contempt for his stepfather, denying what he knows is true—he is becoming a man just like Frank. As he closes the laptop, his mother runs her hand over the piano.

NANCY

I wish you still played. His teacher said he had a God-given talent, that it was a sin for him to quit. We were on our own then, barely able to pay the rent, so she offered to teach for free. Did I ever tell you that, Frank?

WILLIE

You've told him a hundred times. I was in the *fifth* grade. There's no money in playing a piano. If I want music, I'll put on a CD.

120

FRANK

Can't argue with that.

Willie glares at him and storms out of the room

FRANK

It's going to be a long two weeks.

We hear a motorcycle, the roar growing louder as Frank talks.

CUT TO:

Willie looking down at the courtyard, his head framed in the window at the top of the stairs. His POV, over the shoulder.

NANCY (OS)

It's been hard for him. . . .

FRANK (OS)

It's hard for everybody. I'm not a bad guy. He and I are a lot alike.

THUNDER fills the courtyard as Cap pulls up to the gate.

FRANK (OS) (half-shouting)

That's him, isn't it? Shit. just what we need. . . .

Cap kills the engine and dismounts, throwing his leg over the top of the bike. In the sudden quiet, Frank's words echo down the hall.

FRANK (OS)

His jailbird old man.

Willie looks away, his face in profile–ashamed of Cap, ashamed of *himself*–for feeling that way, hating the father who deserted them. But god*damn*–his gaze returning, almost against his will, to the courtyard—*look* at him. *There's* a man who doesn't take anybody's shit. He bolts OUT OF THE FRAME as Cap grabs the barred gate below.

> CAP (shouts)
> Here's the twenty bucks back, Nancy. You probably
> need it to pay your goddamn *attorney*.

He shakes the bars, enraged, *knowing* how foolish he looks, steps back and throws a kick into them, setting off an alarm. A little out of breath now, he looks over the house, the neighborhood, while the mindless alarm warbles and squeals.

> CAP
> Gotta admit. Ole Frank set you up better than I
> ever could.

He wads the bill up and tosses it through the gate. A breeze blows it rolling back out to a stop at his boots. He looks down at it for a long moment, beginning to smile. He laughs, picks it up, and gives the house a little salute.

> CAP (softly)
> OK. (beat) Those were some good years, Nance.
> Take care.

He turns to get on his bike and the alarm goes silent. The gate GRINDS open and Willie steps out. They stand looking at each other, sizing each other up like the strangers they are.

> CAP
> Hi, kid. Sorry about this. You're looking great. I
> heard how well you've been doing. I'm proud of
> you. (beat) For what it's worth. Gotta go.

> WILLIE
> Where to?

CAP

Thought I'd head out to Sturgis. Look around. You and me and your mom all went out there once. Years . . . you must have been six or seven. You probably don't remember. . . .

WILLIE

Sure I do. I remember two other guys. Your friends. One was really big, had a beard and tattoos. The other one . . . he was the *boss* or something.

CAP

Right. They. . . . I better go. Good luck, kid. Tell your mom I won't bother her any more. Tell her I understand.

He turns to get on the bike, struggling with something.

CAP

Tell her. . . .

The intercom at the gate buzzes and we hear Frank's voice through the speaker.

FRANK

Willie. Telephone.

WILLIE (to Cap)

Can I go with you?

It was hard for Willie to *ask* like that. He's used to being the hotshot kid who succeeds at whatever he tries, who *wins*, who *takes*, who has always been given what he wants without having to ask. We can see him stiffen a little now. He's not going to *beg* anyone for anything.

CAP

You don't want to go. It's just a bunch of dumb rednecks. Like me.

WILLIE

I know what I want. I want to go.

INTERCOM (FRANK)

Willie? It's the call you've been waiting for. That job at Microsoft.

CAP

Better get the phone. Jobs are hard to come by these days.

Willie just looks at him, regaining his "attitude."

CAP

You don't have a bike. We can't both. . . .

WILLIE

I rode a bike *up* here. A machine that would blow that old Harley off the road.

INTERCOM–FRANK

The man's waiting. He's willing to give you the sixty K.

CAP

You don't understand. The people at Sturgis. . . .

WILLIE

You *owe* me.

NANCY (OC)

Willie? Are you OK?

124

CAP

I'll be by in an hour. If you're ready, you can go. I won't wait.

EXT.–PIEDMONT STREET–DAY

Cap tools along, the low growl of the Harley invading the exclusive neighborhood. Up ahead the gate at Nancy's house grinds open and the sound of Cap's bike is suddenly drowned out by a SHRIEKING, WAILING engine, powerful but stressed, its character quite different from the Harley's, and Willie rides out on a KILLER NINJA bike, pearly white, patterned with jagged slashes of neon. We *assume* it's Willie hunched down over the gleaming bike. He's wearing multi-color Evel Knievel designer leathers and a Darth Vader helmet.

CLOSE Cap's face as he rides up to the Ninia and peers into the MASK-like helmet.

CAP

That *you* in there?

WILLIE (voice muffled by helmet)

Let's go.

CAP

There's gonna be some pretty tough hombres at this thing. . . .

WILLIE

Don't worry about me. I've got a soloflex and a brown belt in Tae Kwon Do.

The Ninja SCREAMS up the street as Cap watches, unbelieving.

EXT.–HIGHWAY–DAY

Cap and Willie roar down the freeway, a study in contrasts. Willie and his bike sleek, peacock gaudy, the bike squeezing energy from every cc of its hi-compression engine. Knees and elbows hugging the bike, almost prone, helmeted, masked head lowered against the wind, Willie looks as if he is hanging onto a rocket, trying to aim it.

His leathers soft as buckskin, hair blowing back, Cap is whole, become one with machinery and speed. He sits back on the chopped black Harley, legs propped up, relaxed yet still alert, the low compression engine loafing along. Yet they are traveling at the *same speed* as they FLASH past a herd of dairy cows and we lose them in the distance, then HEAR (OC) the banging of a damaged engine, growing LOUDER as we HOLD on the dairy cows, peaceful, safe from the slaughterhouse. Unless milk prices fall.

> POGO (OC)
> I thought we should of checked the oil. We'll be lucky to make fifty more miles.

> WHITEY (OS)
> You should have *checked* it then, not *thought* about it. You're responsible for maintaining the vehicle, including *fluid* levels, godammit.

The van rattles past the cows who look up, startled as we

CUT TO:

EXT.–REST STOP–DAY

A hip young couple in a red Mazda Miata pull into the parking lot. They have a Doberman in the jumpseat. They park next to Cap and Willie's bikes, put the dog on a leash and walk him onto the grass. The woman is very attractive, in shorts and a neon halter top. The man is handsome, looks like he might have played basketball in high school. He wears a LaCoste shirt, white linen shorts and loafers without socks. They look away, as if they've been arguing, while the dog shits in the grass.

> ### WOMAN
> I *told you* he was uncomfortable. Why do you always. . . .

> ### MAN
> *Always.* Whatever it is, I *always* do it. (beat) He's too big for the car. Every time he sees a rest stop, he has to shit.

> ### WOMAN
> *Every* time? Or is it *always.* You. . . .

She stops talking when Cap comes out of the bathroom, his face and neck wet, slicking back his wet hair. Willie follows him, red creases across his face from the helmet he carries like a severed head. They cut across the grass to their bikes, where the man looks away and the woman glares at them, holding the growling dog. Willie smiles at her, says "hi," then slips on dogshit. Flailing his arms and legs, almost falling, the Doberman lunges for him, the woman fighting to hold him back.
Cap is still laughing as they get on their bikes.

> ### CAP
> You charmed her right out of her shorts.

> ### WILLIE
> Very funny. Very sophisticated humor. Dogshit comedy.

At this, Cap laughs harder, and Willie fights back a smile.

> ### WILLIE
> I'm beat. When do we get a motel?

CAP
Motel? We gotta make some *miles* tonight.

CLOSE   The traffic rushing past, the roar like an ocean.

EXT.–REST STOP–DUSK

The same shot, but cars and trucks are turning on their lights. Time
has passed.

WHITEY (OC)
Get a fuckin' dog and you're safe. That's what they
think. All these Yuppies, or whatever you call 'em.

EXT. REST STOP–DUSK

The parking lot is empty except for Whitey's van. There's something in the grass near the bathrooms. It could be the dog, but it's
hard to tell in this light. But even in this light, there's no mistaking
the neon halter top laying next to the van's rear tire.

DUKE (OC)
You should of taken it a little easier on her, Pogo. I
think she was dead by the time it was my turn. I'm
not gonna forget that.

POGO (OC)
I'm sorry, OK? Lighten up, man.

DUKE (OC)
OK. I accept your apology.

POGO (OS)
Remember that chick last summer? The one who
o.d.'d on us?

DUKE(OS)

Nobody knew she was dead till she stiffened up
the next day. (laughs) For a dead chick, she was
pretty good looking.

WHITEY (OC)

Sluts and whores. That's all you ever see anymore.
I'd like to find a nice girl sometime.

FREEWAY–NIGHT

The tail lights of the Miata moving through the dark. When Pogo
speaks it sounds painful, his broken nose stuffed up, his swollen
lip tender.

POGO (OS)

Do you think the deputy agent in charge would be
pissed if he knew we stole this car? Like, would it
make us ineligible or something for a government
job?

WHITEY (OC)

Negative. His instructions were 'whatever it takes
to accomplish the mission.'

INT.– MIATA–NIGHT

CLOSE   An open "Sharper Image" catalogue lit by a flashlight.

DUKE (OS)

It's gonna be so cool to be a DEA agent.

A hand turns the page of the catalogue. PULL BACK TO SHOW
the little convertible stuffed with weapons and equipment. Duke
is jammed in the jump seat with cases of C rations, reading the

catalogue. His death's-head face, eyebrows and eyelashes gone, floating in the reflected flashlight.

WHITEY
We have to find a bigger vehicle.

EXT.–CANYON ROAD–DAY

Cap and Willie pull to the side of a two-lane road, early morning sun breaking over the canyon walls.

WILLIE (voice muffled through helmet)
This is crazy. I'm going back. Find a motel. I'm exhausted. Nobody. . . .

CAP
OK. See you.

WILLIE
Wait a minute.

He pulls off the helmet, HURLS it bouncing down the road like a severed head, and we can see how exhausted he is. His pristine leathers are streaked with grease spots.

WILLIE
Where's the map? I don't have any idea where we are since we left the freeway.

CAP
Don't have a map. Go back about, uh, 25 miles to that Y-intersection where the cattle guard is, take the left fork a couple of miles. . . .

WILLIE
Never mind. Let's go.

CAP

OK. (beat) When I was just a kid, a guy gave me some good advice. "Don't complain, don't make excuses. You'll get along better."

EXT.–GAS STATION–DAY

The Miata pulls in, weapons half-covered with sleeping bags, the three men windblown, beat-up, almost comical if they waren't so frightening. A nightmare 3-Stooges of Pain and Death. An RV, plastered with American flag decals, and a pickup are ahead of them at the two-pump station. The attendant and driver of the RV are having a long conversation in the office. The driver of the pickup is asleep. Whitey honks the horn and the attendant waves without looking at them or interrupting his conversation. Whitey, with some difficulty, pulls his HK out from under the seat and opens the door. Pogo laughs and pulls a pistol.

POGO

Woo woo. *Some* fun now.

DUKE

Not now.

Angry, they turn to Duke, sitting sideways in the jumpseat, and see the police car coming toward the gas station through the small town. They sit back down, staring straight ahead as the patrol car slows, the local cop looking them over. The car drives on to the city limits, turns and passes the station heading the other way. The attendant and the RV driver, an old guy, come out of the office, looking at a map.

ATTENDANT

I'll say it's a good thing you stopped here. There's nothing on that road but *rocks* for the next fifty miles.

A blue-haired old lady, holding a yapping miniature poodle, leans out the window of the RV.

                    WOMAN
        You ever hear of a dog that could sing?

                    ATTENDANT
        No Ma'am.

                    WOMAN
        Well, you're looking at him. Petey, the dog that
        sings. (TO DOG) Petey! Sing *America the Beautiful.*

Petey begins barking out the rhythm of *America the Beautiful* as the RV pulls away, lurching down the road. The driver of the pickup is still asleep, blocking the pumps. Duke is adjusting the C-rations, half-standing, when Whitey throws the Miatta in reverse and PEELS out of the station, almost throwing Duke out of the car.

                    DUKE
        Didn't you hear what the guy said? We don't have
        enough gas to go 50 miles.

INT.–MOUNTAIN HOUSE–DAY

As SHANK pulls two loaves of bread from a big industrial oven, a Marine Corps tattoo on the back of one hand.

                    ALICIA (OS)
        Smells pretty good, daddy. Not bad.

He looks at his half-Mexican daughter, almost a woman. The braces on her teeth make her even more lovely.

                    SHANK
        Say again? Not bad? They're perfect.

ALICIA

Perfect. The smoke alarm didn't go off.

SHANK

Sure. I burned a couple of loaves getting the hang
of this oven.

ALICIA

One or two.

SHANK (LAUGHING)

Yeah, but look at *these*. Whole grain. Healthy stuff.
I should have been a baker. We need some butter,
I think.

CUT TO:

EXT.–GARDEN–DAY

Shank, in old khaki pants and a T-shirt, weeds his tomatoes as his
son ETHAN steps INTO THE FRAME.

SHANK

Your mother would have liked it here.

ETHAN

She always wanted a garden like this. Remember
those tomatoes she grew in coffee cans?

SHANK

Out on the fire escape in that place in Oakland. I
remember how those tomatoes tasted.

ETHAN

You've got a real green thumb, Dad.

SHANK (genuinely pleased)

You really think so?

Ethan smiles, and we see now how much he loves his father.

ETHAN
I *mean* it. Check out those tomatoes. Look at that
corn. You've got it.

CUT TO:

The snarling face of a man-size silhouette target. It rocks with the
sound of shots as we

CUT TO:

Shank, hands on hips, watching Alicia fire a S&W Mdl 29 at the
target. The recoil rocks her, but she's not afraid of it. Ethan stands
to the side holding a Model 12 riot gun. When Alicia fires the last
round, she opens the cylinder, ejects the brass, then holds the gun
by the backstrap.

SHANK
Good. Aim at center of mass, right *here*. That way,
if you're a little off, you'll still hit something. Always
shoot to kill. That's what guns are for.

EXT. COUNTRY ROAD–DAY

A beautiful road–green river purling over boulders, wild flowers
bright even in August, snow-capped mountains in the distance.
Cap and Willie FLASH INTO THE FRAME, past a little sign
that says "Hawk Mesa." A quarter mile down the road, Cap skids
to a stop, turns around and rides back to the sign.

CLOSE   Cap's face. His eyes. Like a man recalling a happy
childhood.

INT.–BUNKER–DAY

It is a solid, windowless room, biker photos and artifacts displayed on the walls and bookcases. A gun safe stands in one corner. Shank sits at a rolltop desk typing some sort of invoice. He glances at a framed photo of a woman who looks a lot like Alicia, only older. It is signed, "Love, Maria."

ALICIA (OC)
Dad? There's bikes coming up the road to the highway.

CUT TO:

Shank standing in the doorway, watching a dust cloud boil down the steep gravel road toward the house. An old M1 Garand leans against the inside of the door jamb.

SHANK
It's OK.

We hear (OC) the *snack* of a pump shotgun being jacked open. Cap and Willie slow as they see the house.

EXT.–BACKYARD–DAY

As he speaks to Shank, Willie looks at Cap, passed out, his head on the table.
WILLIE
He kept saying how much he wanted to talk to you. Like you had all the answers. Then he does this.

Alicia comes from the house with a blanket and pillow.

SHANK
Let's make him comfortable.

He and Willie walk him over to a shade tree and lay him on the blanket. Shank looks down at him a moment, then tucks the pillow under his head.

SHANK

He knew I didn't have any answers.

Cap mumbles something.

SHANK

What did he say?

WILLIE

"Mexico, where the palm trees grow." He's always saying he's gonna go down to Mexico. Drink tequila and sleep on the beach. I remember him saying it when I was a *kid*. He'll never go. Just talk about it. He's a drunk and a loser.

Willie is exhausted, his emotions showing in his eyes. He reminds us of the Willie we first saw playing the piano.

WILLIE

I. I wish he. . . .

SHANK

Come on. Let's take a walk down to the barn.

They take a few steps when Willie stops, manages a smile, and turns to Alicia. Before he finishes his sentence he has to turn away so she won't see the tears in his eyes.

WILLIE

Thanks, Alicia, for lunch and for. . . .

ALICIA

We were glad you could find the house.

136

He and Shank walk through golden, knee-high grass, rolling foot-hills ahead of them, mountains farther off. Tears form in Willie's eyes and run down his cheeks. He tries to dab them off so Shank won't notice.

> SHANK
> Your father's a good man. The best I ever knew.

> WILLIE
> Maybe he used to be. . . .

> SHANK
> He still is. He always will be.

They walk on, the grass hissing against their legs.

> SHANK
> Hawk.

A huge hawk swoops over a fold in the hills, gliding only inches above the grass, skimming the contours of the hill.

> SHANK
> One of the big redtailed hawks that hunt west and
> south of here. They usually work in pairs.

The hawk is magnificent as it banks along the hillside.

> SHANK
> There's his partner.

A second hawk, little more than a speck, circles the blue sky directly above them. The first hawk rolls away from the hill, beating his wings. His broad wings and tail glow deep red as he crosses the sun, spiraling up.

SHANK

I see them almost every time I walk out here. I
know it's just a coincidence, or more likely, because
I'm the only thing moving down here, they're
checking me out. Maybe I'm something they can
kill and eat.

The hawk catches a thermal, riding it up to join the other hawk.

SHANK (CONT)

But I also *know* that they show up when I need
them.

Willie looks dubiously at him. Shank smiles.

SHANK

Whenever I'm feeling fucked-up, hopeless. . . .

WILLIE

You?

SHANK (CONT)

I give my heart to the hawks.

WILLIE (petulant)

What does *that* mean?

SHANK

Look at them.

CUT TO:

THE HAWKS, circling high above them.

SHANK (OC)

Give them your heart.

We watch the hawks do exactly what Shank says, a half-beat behind
his words, as though he commands them.

138

SHANK (OC)
They'll take it from you, circle one more time, then
bank away, and disappear . . . behind the hills.

CLOSE   Willie's upturned face.

INT.–BARN–DAY

Dust sparkles in the beams of afternoon sun slanting through the
walls.

SHANK (OC)
I found this a few days ago. Up there in the foothills.

INT.–WORKSHOP–DAY

Knives of all kinds hang on the walls. Shank holds an old knife in
a beaded sheath. He unsheathes the vicious blade, black with
corrosion.

WILLIE
Pretty far gone.

SHANK
It's good iron.

SERIES OF SHOTS   Shank's hands holding the knife.

SHANK (OC)
It might look bad, but. . . .

Taking the rust off with a spinning steel brush. It's odd-looking
steel.

SHANK (OC)
. . . good iron always stands up.

WILLIE
What kind of blade is that?

139

> SHANK
>
> Damascus, the best there is. They hold it in the fire. . .

Wiping the handle with foaming saddle soap. Polishing the brass hilt until it gleams.

> SHANK (CONT)
>
> . . . until it glows red, then bluish white, burning the flaws out.

Shank works the mottled blade with oil and steel wool.

> SHANK (OC)
>
> Then they fold it over on itself. Layer and hammer it. Heat it again. . . .

The blade is really starting to glow now.

> WILLIE
>
> I haven't cried since I was twelve years old.

> SHANK
>
> Go on to Sturgis. Get to know the world he came from.

CLOSE–THE KNIFE

Shank strokes the blade on an oiled whetstone. As it HISSES over the stone, the hammered layers of steel suggest mountain ranges or breaking waves.

> SHANK
>
> You never know what might happen.

He tests the knife's edge, glancing at Willie, who has fallen asleep from exhaustion. His eyes go wide with surprise when the knife cuts him. He looks down at the blood welling up from a gash on his thumb as we

CUT TO:

EXT.–GRAVEL ROAD–DUSK

The RV from the gas station pulls off the road and lurches into a tree, smashing a headlight and the grill.

INT.–RV–DUSK

Decorated and furnished by a retired working-class couple from Waseka, Minnesota, it's littered with weapons, ammo boxes, coils of rope, C-rations, *Soldier of Fortune* and gun magazines. Duke is driving. Pogo slumps in the passenger seat. Their eyes are dull. Pig eyes. Duke backs up, wrestles with the wheel, then hits the tree again.

WHITEY

Godammit. Get outta there.

He pulls Duke out of the driver's seat, gets in himself and maneuvers the RV into a grove of trees. Through the windshield we can see, way down below, Shank's house.

WHITEY

You got into some quaaludes, didn't you? *Both* of you. You'll have to cut *way* back on drugs if you want those jobs with the DEA. They're gonna want urine samples. (beat) Sleep it off. We'll snatch him tonight.

INT.–SHANK'S HOUSE–NIGHT

Cap is shaking hands with Shank. He's sober now after eight hours of sleep, but a little shaky and shamefaced. Shank is uncomfortable, too.

CAP

I missed all the fun today. But it was good to see you. I think about you a lot–the old days. I think about. . . . Why don't you come with us to Sturgis?

SHANK

I've been out of all that for a long time now. When drugs and money became the *focus* of the club, when it started turning into a *business,* I got out. Maybe you can stop on your way back.

CAP

I can't. I'm planning to head down to, uh. . . .

SHANK

Mexico, where the palm trees grow.

They manage an awkward laugh.

CAP

Down to the Gulf. Try to get on at one of those off-shore oil rigs. Save some money. (beat) I never did get to Mexico.

WILLIE (OC)

Come on, Cap. Let's get on the road.

ALICIA

Sure you don't want to spend the night?

WILLIE

Positive. We should have left hours ago.

Shank slips THE KNIFE into Willie's pack as he shoulders it.

SHANK

Can I give you a hand with this?

Willie takes it from him.

WILLIE

I got it. Thanks for lunch. Glad you two got to spend some time together. Talk about the 'old days.' Gotta go.

CAP

Good to see you kids again. You turned out as pretty as your momma, Alicia. Maria sure would of been proud. . . .

WILLIE (OS)

Cap?

Cap smiles sheepishly, then follows Willie outside. Cap and the kids watch from the porch as they start their bikes. Willie rides out of the yard while Cap takes one last look.

SHANK

Have a good trip, Hermano.

Cap nods and rides off. They watch the two headlights flashing through the trees, the shuddering tailights.

ETHAN

Willie seemed like a good guy this afternoon. He sure turned into an asshole.

SHANK

He was so tired when he got here, all his defenses were down. After a few hours sleep he was back to normal. I saw him cry. He was embarrassed.

ALICIA
He's ashamed of his father. (beat) I wish Cap
wouldn't drink like that. He's so *sweet*.

INT.– RV–NIGHT

No lights. So dark we can barely see, Duke and Pogo snoring in
the back. Whitey is asleep behind the wheel, the big "Captain's
chair" swiveled away from the road.

SHANK (OS)
I showed him how to give his heart to the hawks.

On the dashboard we can just make out the silhouette of a liquor
bottle against the windshield. It flashes like a lighthouse, then goes
dark. We hear motorcycles.

ETHAN (OC)
Aw, dad. You shouldn't talk about that stuff. Now
he thinks you're crazy.

The bottle flashes again, catching the headlights through the trees,
the bikes louder. Then it glows like a lantern, lighting the RV as
the bikes come around the curve.

SHANK (OC)
I showed him how, and he did it. He probably
thinks *he's* crazy.

Out on the road, the bikes rumble past and on up the road, the
roar of their engines muffled by the trees. The RV goes dark again.
We can hear the snores.

EXT.–HILLTOP–NIGHT

Shank sits on a handmade wooden bench, looking at the stars. There are a lot of them. The shadow of the house way down below.

> SHANK
> Shooting star! Pretty one.

He looks down and we see that he's sitting next to a grave.

> SHANK
> Couldn't sleep. I usually go right to sleep these days. (beat) Cap said he wished you were here. (beat) He's all messed up. Got out of prison and every-thing's changed. I don't know what I could do to help him. Willie's turned into an arrogant little dork. Nothing a couple of good ass-kickings wouldn't fix. I'll call Tiny in the morning. . . .

He looks up. Watches the slow-turning stars. A wolf howls in the distance.

> SHANK
> Remember that time we drove into the mountains so you could see snow? (laughs) Eighty degrees down in L.A., but it was *cold*. . . .

We hear the muffled *crack* of gunshots. The *thud* of a shotgun. Blue and orange light flashes from the windows of the house below.

> CUT TO:

The door of the house as Shank bursts through, an axe in his hand. He moves through the house, room by room. Empty. He looks at the bullet-scarred door of the "bunker," hope and fear in his eyes, pounds on the door.

> SHANK (SHOUTS)
> It's me, kids. It's me. Are you OK?

We hear the rasp of the door bolt sliding free. He takes a breath, pushes the door ajar and steps through.

> SHANK
>
> It's me.

SHANK'S POV:

The two kids, behind cover, aim a pistol and a shotgun at him. They flicker in and out of sight in the shadows thrown by a single candle. Alicia puts down her shotgun and runs to Shank, who embraces her. Ethan holds a Model 29 in one hand, his other arm bloody as he comes from behind the gun safe, trying to grin against the pain.

> ETHAN
>
> I'm OK. It hurt at first. But I took the pain. Like you taught me.

He's getting a little woozy as he smiles at his sister.

> ETHAN
>
> I think I hit one of them.

Shank helps him to the chair at his desk and cuts the shirt away with the knife. Shank looks at them, his eyes full of love and pride.

> SHANK
>
> You did good.

> ALICIA
>
> They were after Cap.

Shank's eyes harden as we pull in close and

> DISSOLVE TO:

Shank watching a plane take off at a small airport.

SERIES OF SHOTS:

Shank looking at his garden. It needs water. He looks up at a merciless sun.

The kitchen. The bread Shank baked is green with mold.

CLOSE: The bread is full of worms.

In the bunker, Shank looks at the bullet holes in the door. He opens the gun safe and pulls out a model 12 shotgun. On a shelf inside we can see a set of leathers, colors partly visible on the jacket.
In the grove of trees off the road he looks at the tire marks left by the RV. Picks up broken pieces of the headlight and trim by the tree the RV hit.

DISSOLVE TO:

Shank in the cool, quiet kitchen, a dufflebag in his hand. He's wearing jeans, a khaki shirt, and cowboy boots. He walks out the door into the blazing sun.

INT.–BARN–DAY

Shank walks through the dust sparkling in streaks of sunlight that come through the walls. At the far end of the barn he unlocks a heavy, padlocked door. Inside the shadowy room is something with a tarp over it. He throws the tarp off and we see the biggest, meanest Harley ever put together.
Shank checks the gas lines, etc. He straddles the bike, raises his booted foot.

SHANK
One more time, you son-of-a-bitch.

And kicks it ROARING into life.

BLACK SCREEN:

We HEAR an electric BUZZING and, in the BG, the ROAR of motorcycle engines.

FADE IN:
The snarling face of a BEAR, blood seeping out of its eyes and mouth. A frothy mist blows across the image, then a hand in a surgical glove wipes the blood and antiseptic mist away. It is a tattoo on the inside of A WOMAN'S thigh, beneath the rolled-up leg of her shorts.

PULL BACK TO: DIRTY DOUG, the tattoo artist, working on the tattoo. The wall behind them is covered by a Confederate flag. Painted on the flag a grinning corpse carries another flag and a bloody bayonet, staggering forward as if charging a gun position. His headband, made from yet another flag, pulled down on one side as an eye patch.

WIDER: The "Living Art Tat House," full of cigarette smoke. DIRTY DOUG drops a jeweler's magnifying lens over his eyes and looks down at the tattoo, then over at a photograph of a bear he's copying from a *National Geographic*.

DIRTY DOUG
Why a bear?

WOMAN
For protection.

She leans back in the reclining chair and blows cigarette smoke at the ceiling, a street-tough beauty.

148

DIRTY DOUG
You know what they say over in Montana?

She laughs and glances down at him.

WOMAN
What do they say, Doug?

DIRTY DOUG smiles and looks up, his eyes HUGE behind the magnifying visor. The ROAR of motorcycles grows louder as we

CUT TO:

MAIN STREET–STURGIS–DAY:

Rows of motorcycles are parallel-parked in the middle of the street from one end of town to the other, with another row along each sidewalk. An endless parade of Harleys rumbles up and down the street, ridden by bad-looking bikers and their women, chrome and custom paint jobs flashing in the SUN. Many of the bikes fly American and Confederate flags. A banner over the street reads: "WELCOME BIKERS–BLACK HILLS CLASSIC–STURGIS S.D."

DIRTY DOUG (OS)
Sometimes you eat the bear. Sometimes the bear eats you.
WOMAN (OS)
(laughs)

PULL BACK:

To show the whole glittering length of Main Street and the fairgrounds at the far end of town where the motorcycle sled pull races are in progress, throwing plumes of red dust. Tents and concession stands rise beyond the sled pull area, the tallest is a two-story tower topped by a red, white, and blue conopy. We can just hear a BARKER'S voice, tinny and lost at times in the roar of a thousand Harleys.

                    BARKER
        The wall of death. It's all happening inside. Get
        your tickets now for the first afternoon show. High
        speed dips and dives of death

MAIN STREET–STURGIS–DAY:

The sidewalks are as crowded as the street. Recently painted signs read–SHOWERS 6AM TILL MIDNIGHT–HOG BROTHERS –HERMAN'S BEER GARDEN–PAKLIN BOOT AND SHOE REPAIR. Almost everyone wears denim and black leather, boots and bandannas, chains and tattoos. The men, most of them bearded, walk with a slow, deliberate grace, like dismounted horsemen. The street still looks much like it did in the last century, a frontier town with flat wooden storefronts, the street wide enough for wagon traffic. A scene from some other century, a rendezvous like the Mountain Men used to have, but these outlaws have come out of a wilderness of cities and towns.

SERIES OF SHOTS:

Two laughing bikers doing wheelies, side-by-side.

A bearded biker in buckskins, wearing a top-hat with an Indian headband, riding a throbbing Harley with easy dignity. A woman rides the "pussy-pad" behind him, her breasts jiggling.

A slender girl wearing a halter top, her butt showing through a ragged hole in the seat of her tight, faded jeans.

Two bikers wearing "HUNS MC" colors walk down the sidewalk, abreast. The spurs on their MC boots ring with each step as people move out of their way. A pair of dorky reserve cops step back into a doorway to let them pass.

EXT.–GUNNER'S LOUNGE–DAY:

Cap and Willie in front of the bar, people on the crowded sidewalk breaking like a river around them. The ROAR of thousands of bikes.

CAP (over roar)

You go on ahead, then. I like to do my drinking somewhere a little more quiet. When you get tired of this place, I'll be up the street at the Oasis.

Willie walks in. The place is packed with bikers, a huge, split-level bar with pool tables in the lower section, thick with cigarette smoke. Soundless TV screens on the walls show videos of women in skimpy bikinis firing various kinds of machine guns, sneering, their breasts jouncing, jumping out of the bikini tops from the recoil. The jukebox pumps out LOUD C&W and Heavy Metal. Conversations are SHOUTED.

Bikers wearing their colors push through the crowd–HUNS–BANDIDOS–SONS OF SILENCE–DEVIL'S DISCIPLES. One biker wears a jacket with an embroidered praying Jesus, the rocker beneath it "RIDIN' FOR JESUS." A shirtless biker, his back and the side of his face thick with scar tissue, chews bubble gum, blowing pink bubbles as he limps out the door. A necklace of skulls is tattooed around his neck.

Willie, conspicuous in his designer leathers, takes it all in as he works his way to the bar. It's slowly dawning on him that he's landed in another world. A biker nearby laughs.

BIKER

. . . *hates* long road trips. Sittin' on that little bitty P-pad behind me. Says it bruises her ass for when she wants to wear her short shorts.

151

One of the bouncers, a *very* tall guy with a shaved head, dressed all in black, carries a cast aluminum flashlight as long as a nightstick. White block letters across his T-shirt read IF YOU DON'T SPEAK ENGLISH GET THE FUCK OUT. As he walks past a table, one of the bikers sitting there elbows a friend, grinning, then gestures to the bouncer.

BIKER

What's the flashlight for?

BOUNCER

In case the lights go out.

At the bar Willie stumbles into an emaciated speed-freak, a "crank whore" dressed all in black. She looks like a concentration camp survivor with long blond hair. Her tank top has the words, IF YOU CAN'T BEAT 'EM, BITE 'EM pulled tight over her breasts. There's an evil spark in her sunken eyes, and she smiles like an erotic death's-head with bad teeth. She wears "slave bracelets" and flashing death's-head rings on all her fingers. A snake tattoo writhes from her modest cleavage, but it's the pointed-star nipple rings pressing through her T-shirt that really stop him. She sees that they've caught his attention.

WOMAN
(Talking fast. Spaced-out)

Get your attention, don't they? Plain rings just don't get it anymore, huh-uh. Can't go to a party now without seeing 'em everywhere. So I had to get more elaborate. Novelty designs. Stars, crescent moons. No end to it. See what I'm saying? These are my favorites. When I can't decide, I just put these in. Real T-shirt bumpers, huh? You like 'em?

WILLIE

They're nice ones.

152

WOMAN

You're wondering if it hurt, right? When I pierced
'em. Fuckin' A right it did, but I say, no pain no
gain. That's the way I look at life.

The woman spaces out for a moment, stirring her drink with her
finger. We NOTICE A MAN come through the door.

WOMAN

My old man held an ice cube on 'em to make 'em
numb. He's always there for me, you know? For
his birthday I'm gonna shave my pussy and put a
ring in it. You think he'll like that?

WILLIE

I'm sure he will.

The woman steps back. Looks Willie up and down.

WOMAN

I like that jacket. You look like a real man-about-
town in that outfit. Wanta dance?

As a new song kicks in on the juke box, she laughs and reaches up,
clasping her hands around his neck.

WOMAN

Wanta dance, cowboy?

WILLIE

I'm not much of a dancer.

She smiles up at him and runs her hands down his chest.

WOMAN

I'll bet you dance real good.

153

A a huge biker (MICKEY) comes out of the bathroom behind them, zipping up his jeans. He glares at them.

> MICKEY (TO WOMAN)
> Wait outside.

He straight-arms Willie, slamming him against the bar.

> WILLIE
> Take it easy, man. . . .

> MICKEY
> Don't tell me to take it *easy.*

He raises his meaty hand to shove him again when the MAN we NOTICED coming through the door steps up and taps the biker on the shoulder.

> MAN
> If you'd cut the kid a little slack. . . .

The biker spins around.

> MICKEY
> The fuck do you. . . ?

> MAN (CONT)
> I'd sure appreciate it.

It's Shank. The biker's rage evaporates. He drops his hands, calls over his shoulder to the woman.

> MICKEY
> As you were, bitch. Get back here.

He holds his hands up, palms out.

MICKEY
Sorry man, didn't recognize you. I come out of the
shitter, fuckin' place is dark. . . .

He waves one hand in front of his eyes.

MICKEY
No idea he was a friend of yours.

(to Willie)
You two were probably talking, having a drink.
Sorry to interrupt.

Willie tries to hide how shaky he is when he turns to Shank, but
Shank hears it in his voice, sees his knees quiver. So does the biker.
Shank only nods when Willie speaks.

WILLIE
Thanks, I suppose, but I could have handled it on
my own.
MICKEY (to Shank)
I guess I'll get in the wind if. . . .

He grabs the crank whore's arm and shoves her toward Willie.

MICKEY
You two have a good one, then.

Starts to walk away.
WILLIE
No thanks.
MICKEY
You sure? We've got . . . *she's* got a room over in
Spearfish. You two could. . . .

WILLIE
Do you really think I'd have anything to do with
somebody like her?

Shank sees the hurt in the tough crank whore's eyes. His manner
is plain-spoken but quite formal when he speaks.

SHANK
I was hoping that I could buy you a drink before I
had to leave?

He glances at Mickey for his approval, makes a very subtle bow to
the crank whore and takes her arm. He gives the biker a *look* and
walks to the bar, speaking over his shoulder to to Willie.

SHANK
You're on your own, kid.

The crowd's been watching all this, and they open into a circle
around Willie and the biker. Willie assumes a very competent karate
stance, but the fear is still in his eyes. There is laughter from the
crowd.

CROWD
Looks like he's gonna try some of that kung foo
fighting.

CROWD #2
He got off at the wrong bus station with those
leathers. Must of thought this was Las Vegas.

Everyone in the bar except Willie knows he's already lost this fight.
What happens next is just a painful formality. Willie screams a kai,
and moves through a "form," again quite competently. But Mickey
just moves out of the way and Willie slashes and kicks at empty
air. Most martial arts are like dance forms perfected in the safety
and predictability of a gym, not very useful on the street.
Mickey wades in and knocks him down. Willie gets up and tries a
kick, but Mickey grabs his leg and slings him into the bar. Willie

156

gets up, bloody, swinging wildly now, and gets knocked down. Mickey glances back at Shank who only shrugs, so he picks Willie up, backhands him a couple of times, and lets him fall. He's bleeding over one eye, from his ear, and blowing blood bubbles from his nose. He gets to his knees, then to his feet. Mickey is out of breath, splattered with Willie's blood.

CROWD(laughs)
Gonna wear you down, Mick.

CROWD #2
Better *pace* yourself.

Mickey smiles grimly at the crowd, pins Willie against the bar, punches, then knees him in the stomach, butts him with his forehead and lets him fall.

CROWD
That's enough, man.

CROWD #2
Fuck *that*. He gets what he gets, man.

Mickey kicks him, awkwardly. He steps back, cocks his leg to seriously put the boots to him, when the crank whore comes up behind Mickey.
WOMAN
Mickey? Honey. . . .

MICKEY (snarling)
OK, *what?*
WOMAN
Shank would like to buy you a drink.

He looks over at the bar where Shank smiles, nods, a gesture meaning "that's enough."

157

WOMAN

He's a real gentleman.

Mickey nods his thanks, knocks back the drink, sets the glass on the bar.

MICKEY

I had the honor of meeting you once down in Oakland. . . .

He almost offers his hand, then snatches it back.

MICKEY

Of course, you wouldn't remember me. I was just a punk.

He pushes the crank whore toward him.

MICKEY

If *you'd* like to strap her on. . . .

SHANK

As much as I'd like to spend the afternoon with Gloria, I can't. I have to meet some people. (to Gloria) I heard you say you liked that jacket. It's yours. I know he'd like you to have it.

A couple of bikers in the crowd hold Willie up and pull him out of the jacket. Gloria tries it on, looks down at herself, smiling.

GLORIA

That blood will come right out with cold water when it's still fresh like that.

Mickey pulls a pair of handcuffs off his belt and snaps one cuff over the crank whore's wrist.

158

MICKEY

Lazy Eight Motel. Room Five. She'll be cuffed to
the bed if you change your mind.

He pulls her with him, out the door as she grins at Shank, then
waggles her tongue at him. Her silhouette shimmers, wraith-like,
as she disappears into the sunlight with MICKEY who, we see, is
wearing DEVIL'S DISCIPLES colors, a devil standing in a flaming
doorway. Circling the back of Mickey's neck, tattooed in thick
block letters—100% PECKERWOOD.

LESTER

THE KID'S ALL RIGHT.

The words BOOM out from the back of the place and LESTER,
road captain of the Oklahoma City Bandidos, walks out of the
shadows. The Bandidos claim they can hear his shouted directions
at 30 mph on the interstate. He's as big as Tiny, wearing a torn
and stained woven poncho with the Bandidos' colors on it. Hands
on hips, he watches with interest as Willie, shirtless now, gets to
his feet and stumbles to one side, then the other, as if he was on a
rolling deck.

LESTER

MICKEY'S GONE, KID. RELAX. HE'S ABOUT AS BAD AS
THEY COME. (laughs) I LIKE THIS KID. NOT VERY
SMART, BUT HE'S GOT BALLS. I BEEN THINKING ABOUT
PUTTING MY COLORS ON A NEW PONCHO. DOES ANY
OF THE MEMBERSHIP THINK THAT'S . . . *INAPPRO-
PRIATE? (laughs)*

He looks around. No one objects, so he tears his colors off the
filthy vest and tosses them to Willie.

LESTER

GIVE 'EM HELL, KID.

He walks toward the door with an entourage of bad-looking Bandidos, then notices Shank for the first time.

LESTER
SHANK. GOOD TO SEE YOU.

They shake hands.

LESTER
YOU SEE THAT KID KEEP GETTING UP SO HE COULD GET THE SHIT KICKED OUT OF HIM MORE OFTEN? HE MIGHT TURN OUT OK. IF MICKEY DIDN'T GIVE HIM A BRAIN HEMORRHAGE OR RUPTURE HIS SPLEEN.

Lester and the Bandidos go out the door, all ROARING with laughter. Willie is still trying to find the armholes in the poncho.

SHANK
Willie. I'm going to look for your dad. We'll meet you around five at . . . that wall of death place. Are you OK?

WILLIE
Yes, sir. Five o'clock.

INT.–OASIS LOUNGE–DAY

A dark, almost grim place for more serious drinkers. We hear a few phrases of a rock/heavy metal version of "Cap's song," before the mechanical arm SLAPS another record on the jukebox. Shank orders a beer from one of the bartender/bouncers, 250 pounds of muscle with a baby face and thick glasses. All the bouncers look like steroid-shooting high-school defensive linemen. It's difficult to make out the faces of the other drinkers at the bar.

Someone starts shouting over by the pool tables.

> CAP
>
> What do you mean, you can't "serve me" anymore?
> You're not *serving* me. I give you money and you
> pour me tequila.

He has a billiard ball in each hand that he *cracks* together as a pair
of bouncers move in.

> CAP
>
> And if any of these Baby Huey fuckin' bouncers
> get in my way, they're gonna be chewing on 9-balls.

The bartender pulls a sawed-off baseball bat from beneath the bar
and smiles like the Homecoming Prince at the Senior Prom.

> BARTENDER
>
> Excuse me, folks. I'll be right back.

> SHANK
>
> I'd appreciate it if you'd let me talk to him.

> BARTENDER
>
> Go on ahead then, sir, but if he won't listen, I have
> to do my job.
>
> SHANK
>
> Cap.

Cap recognizes the voice, but it takes him a few seconds to focus
on Shank.

> CAP
>
> You caught me at a real bad time.

> SHANK
>
> All we have to do is leave, and everybody will be
> happy.

CAP

I won't be happy. I want another drink.

Shank hands the bartender a twenty dollar bill.

SHANK

One more? Then we'll go. Keep the change. (to Cap) Comin' up, Cap.

Sparks arc on a stun gun one of the bouncers carries.

CAP

You're gonna wish your momma never bought you that toy, Archie.

BOUNCER

Don't talk about my mom. Anyway, she didn't buy it for me. And my name's not 'Archie,' either.

The bartender sets the tequila on the pool table.

BARTENDER

There you go, sir.

Cap puts the billiard balls down and tosses the drink back.

CAP

OK, Arch. Be careful with your new appliance.

On the way out they see Jensen, the road captain who replaced Cap, at a table with some Berserker "prospects."

JENSEN

I heard they let you out.

He grins at the prospects, gray-faced losers in their 30s and 40s with long dirty hair and speed cankers around their eyes and mouths.

162

JENSEN

I told you about *Cap,* didn't I? One of the old timers.
You learn a trade up there at the graystone hotel?

He laughs as they walk out the door, the prospects joining in.

EXT.–MAIN STREET–DAY:

Shank and Cap walk up the boardwalk, the sun bearing down,
glittering off the hundreds of unmuffled bikes that roar past, filling
the air with diesel fumes. Cap is pale, shaky, his eyes bloodshot.
Shank steps aside to let three BANDIDOS pass, their boots shaking
the boardwalk. One of them looks back at him, trying to place
him, then walks on.

SHANK

I need to talk to you.

CAP

I should have killed him. I would have done less
time on a murder rap. (beat) OK. But let's get the
fuck out of here. Too many people, man. Makes
me nervous.

Up the boardwalk, past "Hog Brothers," piled up at the entrance
to an out-of-business shoe store, several weeks worth of unopened
newspapers are turning yellow. Cap stops and picks up one of the
more recent ones. He folds it open to a photo of a man who looks
like Gordon Liddy. The caption reads:

Convicted Justice Department official killed in prison
Stabbed to death by former homosexual lover
who was himself killed by guards.

CAP

I know this guy. They put him in my cell for a
couple of weeks when he first got there, a few weeks

before I got out. They came and got him in the
middle of the night. Some assistant warden was with
them. All pissed off. Put him in isolation. Fuckin'
guy's dead.

They pass one of the "beer gardens"–hammered-together picnic
tables in a vacant lot–when Cap looks at the paper again.

CAP

What are they talking about? He wasn't a faggot.
He was a standup guy. Smart, too. He knew everything about history.

Cap throws the yellowing newspaper into a garbage can full of
plastic beer cups and half-eaten hot dogs.

EXT.–MAIN STEET–DAY

Willie, in his filthy vest and designer leather pants, walks smiling
down the boardwalk. Beat-up as he is, he's filled with something
like euphoria. Through the beating he took, and the praise that
followed, he discovered a powerful new emotion. It was almost
like being in love.
As he passes an alley, he glances down it to see INDIO and a big
biker. The biker is drunk, advancing on Indio as she circles around,
walking backward. She wears Levi's and a blue work shirt, looking
out of place here in Sturgis. Her parents were Mormon missionaries
killed at one of their missions. She learned to ride a bike from her
big brother–has a real knack for it. He was killed in "Desert Storm,"
driving one of those Special Forces dune buggies on recon way
behind the Iraqi lines. She met the BARKER when they came
through town for the county fair.

BIKER

Come on, little sister, let's you and me get real.

INDIO

You're real enough. I'm convinced. Let's leave it at that.

BIKER

Come to your daddy.

Willie makes eye-contact with Indio, and that stops him.

WILLIE

Do you need some help with that guy?

The biker grabs Indio's arm then looks at Willie.

BIKER

You been watching too many movies bro. The bitch was *born* for this. She loves it. Or do you want to strap her on, too?

Indio jerks free and steps between them, glaring at Shank.

INDIO

If I need help I'll call the police. Who are *you?* Maybe *stupid* here is my husband. This is a little fantasy we like to act out.

Willie holds up his hands and backs out to the street, but he watches them as Indio turns back to the biker.

INDIO (mimicking him)

'The bitch was born for it.' *You've* been watching too many movies.

BIKER

Let's get serious.

As he fumbles with his belt, Indio pulls out a can of mace and wets him down. He stumbles blindly around, rubbing his eyes, cursing and trying to grab her. She sprays him again, then picks up a long-neck beer bottle and starts hitting him, in the forearms and wrists as he tries to grab her. She hits him in the shin, and when he grabs his leg, she hits him on the back of the neck, knocking him down. She maces him again as he vomits and rolls into a fetal position.

                    BIKER
        OK. Jesus Christ! I quit. I'm sorry.

                    INDIO
        A whiner. I expected that.

She walks to the street where Willie stands watching.

                    INDIO
        Can I do something for you?

                    WILLIE
        No Ma'am.

                    INDIO
        You look awful.

Willie watches her walk away, and just before she disappears into the crowd she turns and looks at him for a long moment, her face still full of anger. But then—she can't help it—she smiles and gives him a little salute before turning and walking out of sight as the biker staggers out of the alley, tears and snot running down his face, vomit in his beard.

                    BIKER
        Fuckin' woman's lib, man. Try satisfy 'em, and they
        go *off* on you.

EXT.–MILITARY CEMETERY–DAY

166

Thousands of white granite markers rise in endless columns on the green hills. A huge American flag ripples in the breeze as bikes upshift and whine past out on the interstate.

CAP (OS)

. . . Ethan's gonna be OK?

CUT TO:

Cap sitting against a granite marker, that reads

CALVIN ANDERSON
SGT
US ARMY
INDIAN WARS
DEC 7 1847–MAY 11 1870

CAP (CONT)

I'm sorry, Shank. I don't know *who* those guys are.I thought it was some kind of mistake up in Oakland.We can talk to the club. Maybe they can help you.

SHANK

Maybe? Of course they'll help. It's still the Berserkers.

CAP

It's not the *same* club. You were right about that, only things are worse than you think. (beat) But we can talk to them.

He stands stiffly up, using the grave marker as a handhold.

CAP

I sure never expected to live this long. *Look* at me, man. What good am I to anybody? I wake up every morning and think. . . . Fuck it. I need a drink.

167

Seems like the only place I feel at home any more is in cemeteries.

They walk down through the wild flowers, Cap limping.

> CAP
>
> I was sorry to hear about Maria. Word is she showed a lot of class.
>
> SHANK
>
> More than me. Watching her die all those months.

Across the road from their bikes, a blue-haired old lady sits in a wicker chair in front of the little administration building. Cap waves and Shank sees the knotted, purple scar on Cap's forearm.

> CAP
>
> Thanks for taking such good care of all these guys. I know they're grateful. I hope *I* end up in a place like this.

The lady points to a padlocked collection box. A flyer taped to it reads: Preserve the Indian War Section. Help us remind Washington that our heroes deserve to rest in dignity.

> LADY
>
> Would you care to contribute to the fund? If we can't convince Congress to intervene, the developers will remove all the dead in the Indian War Section, rebury them in a pasture 30 miles from all their friends here, and start building. Nobody visits those old graves anymore, so they think they can get away with it.

She points off to yellow plastic tape fluttering in the breeze, and earth moving equipment.

CAP (embarrassed)
I'm broke right now.

LADY
We know you'd help if you could.

Shank and Cap walk to their bikes, Cap cursing himself. Shank looks at the scar on Cap's arm.

SHANK
You used to have the Berserker colors tattooed there.
CAP
I cut 'em off one night when I was fucked up. It didn't heal up too good, did it? (laughs) I almost died of blood poisoning. I guess you could say I didn't adjust too good after I got out of the joint. My daddy knew it, predicted it all, the day I left Mystic, Georgia.

CLOSE–THE SCAR. Traces of the tattoo, the Berserker colors, are still visible around the angry scar.
CUT TO:

HUNDRED DOLLAR BILLS, HUGE, CLOSE, filling the screen.

As we HOLD ON THE BILLS, they begin to ripple, like piled autumn leaves in a faint breeze. They go still. Something, we see something else in the bills. *Looking* at us. A black, unblinking eye. A MOUSE falls INTO THE FRAME, down through the money, kicking as if it is trying to swim, and the eye vanishes in an EXPLOSION of money and we pull back slightly to see SNAKES, dozens of them, swimming through hundred dollar bills. Rattlesnakes coursing, gliding, *hissing* through the bills toward the mouse where they twine into a hungry pulsing cluster.

169

> VALLEY GIRL GROUPIE #1 (OC)
> Oh, gross.

INT.–AIRSTREAM–DAY

The biggest, most expensive Airstream trailer made, packed with the most expensive furniture, stereo equipment, big screen TVs, etc. Somehow though, it looks cheap. It's the rolling office of the current President of the Berserkers MC, Voker, "The Joker." Voker and the club have more money than they can spend, but Voker is still the same white trash he was back when he'd sleep passed out on some filthy kitchen floor, or curled up and content on the concrete floor of the Oakland City Jail.

A huge aquarium, filled with money and snakes, dominates the front room of the Airstream. Voker and "Bolt" Bolten watch as two naked groupies, Valley girls who hitched a ride outside Tarzana, feed the snakes. Bolton is a Dolf Lundgren/ Brian Bosworth type actor who does low-budget biker movies. Voker *used* to like having him around, a real celebrity. Bolton likes hanging around because there's free women and dope and liquor. And because, as he tells people in Hollywood, "These dudes are so *real*, man." There are Bolt Bolton movie posters on the wall.

Groupie #1 reaches gingerly into a Chinese food take-out box, then jerks her hand away.

> GROUPIE #2
> *Jenn*ifer. Just *do it*. You know how.

Groupie #1, Jennifer, reaches back in and pulls a white mouse out of the box, holding it by the end of the tail.

> JENNIFER
> Oh, gross, gross, gross.

> "BOLT" BOLTEN
> Feed the pets, bitch.

Bolton grins over at Voker as if to say, "Am I cool, or what?" He holds the grin now, as if he's saying, "I mean, are *we* cool?" Voker manages a smile, then looks down unhappily at his beer belly. But that's good enough for Bolton, who looks back at the groupies. Jennifer drops the mouse and both girls hop, shrieking, from foot to foot, their buttocks' flexing, as the money boils with snakes.

> JENNIFER
> I *hate* touching mice. They're so . . . *nerdy*. Like, the way they just *expose* their assholes.

> BOLTON
> You bitches are turning me on. (to Voker) Are they a *turn on*, bro? Sex and death, man. *You* know what I'm talkin' about.

Voker nods. Through a bedroom door we can see an elaborate, absurd circular bed. Strings of blinking red lights twine around the pillars holding up a mirror/canopy. A phone rings twice, OC. K-Mart, Voker's Lieutenant from the old days, calls from another room.

> K-MART (OC)
> Hey, boss. It's Stafford. Says it's an emergency.

> BOLTON (TO VOKER)
> That fuckin' lawyer again, man? Tell him you're in a *meeting*.

> VOKER
> That's a good idea, Bolt. I'd *do* that, but I'm a little worried about jail time, you know what I mean?

> BOLTON
> OK, man, but he's gonna think you got nothing better to do. . . .

VOKER

Than stay out of jail? He's right. The motherfucker
must of read my mind.

Bolton is surprised by Voker's tone, but before it can sink into his
steroid ego, Voker checks his anger.

VOKER

I loved that scene in *Chrome Wheels,* the one where
you. . . .

THE WALL OF DEATH–AFTERNOON:

A two-story, wood-slat tower with stairs curving up to the walkway
around the top. A BARKER stands out in front, with a microphone,
his voice booming out of the PA system, fast, but smoothly cadenc-
ed, an almost hypnotic rap. In the BG we see the RV bouncing
past on bad shocks.

BARKER

The Wall of Death. It's all happening inside. High
speed motorcycle thrills and chills. Free-hand trick
and fancy acrobatic riding. Dips and dives of death.
The finest in motorcycle entertainment. We're here
to thrill and entertain you. If you're not satisfied,
come on down and see the lady in the ticket booth
and she'll give you your two dollars back. . . .

CUT TO:

INDIO taking tickets on a little platform halfway up the stairs.
The ticket dispenser next to her is painted with a death's-head.
Dollar bills, folded lengthwise, fan out from her fingers. A smiling
fat guy wearing an "I SURVIVED STURGIS" T-shirt holds out
two dollars.

FAT GUY
Some crowd, huh?

INDIO
Enjoy the show.

Indio manages a smile back, making the guy's day. When she turns
for the next two dollars, it's Willie holding them out.

INDIO
Well, look here.

WILLIE (laughs)
Me again. Hoped I'd see you again, but I didn't
expect to. Do you work here?

INDIO
Take tickets, balance the books.

WILLIE
Guess your boyfriend does the riding, huh?

INDIO
Enjoy the show.

Willie nods at her and starts up the stairs as she hands a ticket to
the next person in line, all business again. Then, at the same
moment, they each turn for another look, and catch each other
looking.

BARKER (BG)
Last call. We're giving the safety instructions on
the inside. When the line ends, the show begins. If
you miss this one, there's two more this evening.

Indio removes the ticket holder and closes the money box as we
hear BOOTS on the stairs behind her.

173

WHITEY (OS)
How'd you like to ride *my* motorcycle?

INDIO
(NOT BOTHERING TO LOOK AT WHO IS SPEAKING)
You'll have to wait for the next show.

Indio tucks the moneybox under her arm and turns to go down
the stairs, but freezes, holding her breath, when she makes eye
contact with Whitey. Duke and Pogo stand just behind him,
blocking the stairs.

WHITEY
You won't make me wait *twice*. Once I've put it *to*
you. You never met anybody like me.

Duke laughs his phony, measured laugh. POGO, wearing his
Smokey-the-Bear hat, grabs his own crotch and grunts.

WHITEY (HISSES)
I'll split you wide open. Then we'll see how you
do with that smartass mouth.

WILLIE (OS)
I forgot to ask you your name.

Willie hasn't heard the exchange. He smiles as he comes down the
steps. Until Whitey spins and looks down at him.

WILLIE (CONT)
Is everything OK?

WHITEY
As long as you keep walking down those stairs,
pissant. (beat) Where's your shit-eating grin now?

DUKE (LAUGHS)
Sneaked up on you, Whitey. Woo Woo.

WHITEY
I saw him, goddamnit.

Whitey pulls a cheap knife, the edge ruined by a grinding stone, but scary looking, as Shank comes up the stairs.

SHANK
You got a problem here?

WHITEY
You got a problem if you don't mind your own business.

A subtle change comes over Shank as he looks at Whitey—a kind of calmness, as if something has shifted gears within him. There's a scary kind of joy growing within him. Another couple of seconds and maybe he can start to *get even* for his wife's slow death, for what has happened to his friend Cap, for the attack on his children. Whitey doesn't see it, but Duke, as he is about to laugh, does see it and the laugh dies in his throat as Shank slides into an easy defensive position.

SHANK
You gonna do something with that knife?

And now Whitey is beginning to sense it too.

BIKER #1 (OS)
Hey. When's the show start?

BIKER #2 (OS)
Show time. Time to roll.

We pull back and see a bunch of bikers looking down from the walkway atop the wall of death. As Whitey pockets the knife, he surrenders eye-contact with Shank, then looks at Indio.

WHITEY
I'll see you again. I *like* you.

They go down the stairs, shoving past Willie. Shank watches them go.

SHANK
Guys like that, you just want to shoot 'em right away. Don't even talk to them. (beat) Cap and I have to talk to some people tonight. You got something to do?

Willie and Indio exchange a look.

WILLIE
Yes, sir.

DISSOLVE TO:

TOP OF THE WALL OF DEATH

Looking DOWN where the BARKER climbs through a little opening at the base of the wall, and picks up a microphone. The bottom of the pit is oil-soaked dirt and dead grass.

The walkway up top is jammed with funky bikers and their women. One of the women pulls her shirt up to show her tits, and everyone laughs and applauds. Another woman takes up the challenge and pulls *her* shirt up. Her tits are bigger, and they have *tattoos* on them. The crowd cheers.

Indio, all in her fancy leathers now, crawls through the opening in the wall and starts her Indian motorcycle, the gas tank painted like an American flag. The BARKER fits a little door into the opening, and looks up at the crowd.

176

BARKER
Ladies and gentlemen, please stand away from the
wall.

Indio revs the Indian and begins to spiral up the wall. The engine
dies and she glides back down. The crowd laughs.

CROWD
Get her a motor scooter.

CROWD #2
I'd like to do some wrench-ing on *her*.

Indio looks up at the second guy and shakes her head.

INDIO
Everybody wants something, but I don't
see any chance of *that,* big guy.

As the crowd laughs, Indio and the Barker huddle over the bike.
We can see that she's still a little shaky from the encounter on the
stairs. The Barker points something out, and Indio puts a wrench
on it, then starts the bike again.

BARKER
These old Indians and Harleys–that one there is a
1923 Indian–are kind of temperamental. I'll bet
one or two of you have had a bike break down.

We get a glimpse of Shank in the laughing crowd.

BARKER (CONT)
Any bike will break down. Like they say, if it's got
tits or wheels, you'll have trouble with it.

Indio looks at him as she thumbs her wrench open.

BARKER (CONT)

Some say that, but I don't. Lay a bike down here
and it's a serious down. You're up there *sideways.*
Tires blow out, chains snap, grease on the wall
throws you down, but hell, what's life without a
few broken legs.

The crowd cheers as Indio gets the bike going smoothly, and starts
up the wall again. She reaches the red line in the middle of the
wall and circles it–er-RAH, er-RAH, er-RAH on the unmuffled
bike, making the whole structure shudder and shake–the crowd
quiets down, watching. She's not *bad.*

BARKER

And now she'll ride, at speeds of forty miles per
hour, to the very top of that red line, then dip away.

And Indio does. She arcs up to the lip of the wall, shallow arcs at
first, not that close to the lip, then steeper and faster and closer to
the safety-cable stretched around the edge, the wall rocking at the
top of each arc until she comes so close to the edge that people
step back, worried that she'll flip over the top and hit them. It's
crazy. Indio slows and drops to the middle line, cruising around it
now, as the crowd cheers and applauds. These rough bikers take
their arms from around their girl friends, stick their cigarettes in
their mouths, and *applaud,* the tattoos on their biceps and shoulders
flexing as they clap.

BARKER

The dips and dives of death, ladies and gentlemen,
without the use of handlebars or controls–high
speed motorcycle entertainment at its finest.

Indio picks up speed, the wall shuddering, arcing higher and
sharper. She takes her hands from the handlebars, guiding the bike

with her knees, holding her arms up and out in a victory gesture.
Er-RAH, er-RAH. Now she slips one leg over the gas tank and
rides side-saddle, still arcing as–GODDAMN–the crowd goes
crazy. They hold dollar bills over the edge of the cable as she
zooms up and back, climbing and diving, snatching the bills out of
their hands, out of the men's teeth as they lean over the edge,
putting their faces down toward the screaming steel. Strangers in
the crowd look at each other, grinning and shaking their heads.
Indio slows, just cruising now–*whap whap*–as we see Willie looking
down at her. Each time she goes around they have a moment of
eye contact–*whap whap*.

> BARKER
> Thank you, ladies and gentlemen. And now, in just
> a moment, the Australian Pursuit Race!

The Barker cranks up an old Harley, waves to the crowd, and
spirals up to the center line, just in front of Indio. The two bikes
take a turn together, then Indio's Indian roars and she arcs up
over the top of the Barker. He laughs, guns the Harley, and goes
over the top of Indio. Round they go, arcing back and forth over
one another and the crowd admires their bravery so much they
almost want them to stop–that's enough. No more chances–but
they keep arcing behind and over and down past each other,
avoiding collision by inches. When they drift down to the bottom
of the pit, the crowd cheers.They've gotten their money's worth.

> BARKER
> Two more shows, ladies and gentlemen, before we
> close it up and head south.

DISSOLVE TO:

EXT.–MIDWAY–DUSK:

Thunderheads loom in the western sky, but here the setting sun
streams through the dust of the Fairgrounds. Shank and Cap sit on
their idling bikes, looking up at the hills. For the first time, Shank
is wearing his colors.   CAP
> Indian country. Sioux war parties rode out of those

hills a hundred years ago.
A group of young guys walk past, not seeing Shank's colors.

SHANK

Well, hell, let's go on up then.

YOUNG GUY #1

The Berserkers are up there, man.

SHANK

Who's that?

YOUNG GUY #2

Are you kidding? The Berkserkers. Nobody goes
up there.

On the sound of their bikes

DISSOLVE TO:

Campfires and a full moon, like an ancient army camped for the
night before battle, except for the band playing rock music on the
stage far below in the campground where thousands of motorcycles
roar, headlights flashing, dust rising in the moonlight. Shank and
Cap ride INTO THE FRAME, and we see that guards, back in
the treeline, are watching.

CUT TO:

A huge fire made of saplings and railroad ties lighting the hillside.
The bikers look like barbarians before battle, beards and long hair,
boots, sheath knives and chains, their thick corded arms dark with
tattoos. A refrigerated trailer, Berserker colors painted on the side,
rumbles in the shadows. It is filled with sides of beef and kegs of
beer. A pig roasts over the fire pit, its drippings flaring up, illuminating the biker women who stand in the heat, turning the spit. Bikers
climb the steep face of the hillside at the back of the camp, their
rear wheels throwing dirt. And now we can see other bikers, in

180

shadow and sudden silhouette, shotguns slung over their shoulders or cradled in their arms, watching. As Shank and Cap pull into the light, kill their bikes and dismount, gunmen close up security on the trail behind them.

VOKER, the current club president, walks out of the shadows towards them. He was just one of the brothers when Shank was president of the club, but then he made some Hollywood drug connections in the '80s and money started rolling in. They have more money now than they can use. They have to think of things to waste it on. Under all his hype, Voker still thinks of Shank as the President.

                    VOKER
    Clark. . . . Spider, looked good today. . . .

He shakes hands with Shank, and embraces him.

                    VOKER
    A great honor to have you in camp. (beat) Cap.

                    CAP
    I'm gonna take a walk.

As Cap walks away, several of the Berserkers go over and shake his hand or slap him on the shoulder. Voker gestures to the front rank of Berserkers, full members, and walks Shank to them–an outlaw biker receiving line–and Shank shakes hands, clasping some, as Voker introduces them.

                    VOKER
    Bad Bill, Dresser Jim.

                SHANK(SMILES)
    I remember when you put those two Fresno cops
    in the hospital on the Labor Day run.

Dresser Jim smiles, remembering.

                    181

INT.–AIRSTREAM–NIGHT

Shank looks around the gaudy trailer, his eyes narrowed in that Clint Eastwood squint of disgust and disbelief, nodding in agreement with Voker. Voker's tone boasting, yet with a slight undertone that *wants* Shank's approval.

> VOKER
> Come quite a way from the old clubhouse in Fontana.

Shank hears a clicking behind one of the doors. He looks at Voker for permission, and opens it to find K-Mart feeding greenbacks through a money counting machine, the running total flashing in LED numbers.

> K-MART
> Shank! Great to see you. Hang on *just* a second while I . . . *there.*

K-Mart finds a place to put the count on "hold," stands up and shakes hands with Shank.

> K-MART
> I was gonna come out and see you, but I had to finish counting this damn money. (lowers voice) We got this Hollywood drug connection, more money than we can spend. They're doing crank now instead of cocaine. (normal tone) Gimme an abrazo. It's been a long time.

They embrace, step back and look at each other, both of them clearly moved. K-Mart's smile sours at Voker's announcement.

> VOKER
> Shank. Somebody here I want you to meet. "Bolt" Bolten. That's right.

Chrome Wheels. Amazon Biker Kill. He spends time
with us.

Bolton is half-dressed, his steroid-swollen muscles gleaming. He
towers over Shank, standing *too* close, his eyes dilated with speed,
a touch of arrogance in his voice.

> BOLTEN
> Voke' here told me about you, man. Says you were
> real *bad* in your day.

Shank is apparently relaxed, pleasant. He looks down at the floor,
then smiles up at Bolten. Voker watches nervously.

> SHANK
> Not me. I was more of a diplomat.

We follow Shank's gaze to one of the movie posters, and HOLD
ON THE POSTER.

> BOLTEN (OC)
> Oh yeah? I hear all these stories, *Shank* this and
> that, *Badass* Shank. . . .

> SHANK
> Stories. That's all it is.

CUT TO:

Bolton's grin.

> VOKER (NERVOUSLY)
> Tell him who you used to date, Bolt.

> BOLTEN
> He doesn't care about that, man.

> SHANK
> A star? Is he a movie star? Who?

After a long moment, Bolten decides it was just a slip of the tongue when Shank said "he."

> BOLTEN
> The most recent one? Me and Madonna been getting it on. . . .

> VOKER
> Madonna. You believe that?

> BOLTEN
> I'd like to stick around and talk some more, man, but I got unfinished business to take care of.

As he grabs his crotch and looks toward the bedroom door.

> SHANK
> A real pleasure to meet you.

Bolten walks to the bedroom, closes the door.

> VOKER
> He's not a bad guy once he gets to know you. Great Hollywood stories. (beat) He's the one with all the connections.

> SHANK (SADLY)
> Voker the Joker.

Shank indicates a battered hand-carved plaque almost hidden by the clutter at the end of the trailer. It reads, LOYALTY AND HONOR–BERSERKERS MC.

> SHANK
> From the old clubhouse in Fontana. (beat) We're just white trash. Born white trash, and that's all we'll ever be if we forget *that.*

184

EXT.–THE WALL OF DEATH–NIGHT

The action is across the campground where the big stage gleams, an island of light, hundreds of cigarettes glowing in the darkness surrounding it. The snarling heavy-metal music reaches us here in the moon-shadow of the Wall of Death where a gust of wind kicks up dust and blows a beer can end-for-end over the sunbaked dirt. Faint yellow light shows through the slats of the Wall of Death.

> INDIO (OS)
> My brother. He taught me to ride, and I discovered I had this weird *ability* for it. (beat) Cal loved bikes.

EXT.–CAMPGROUND–NIGHT

Willie and Indio on a knoll overlooking the Wall of Death.

> INDIO (CONT)
> He joined Special Forces so he could drive one of those combat dune buggies. (beat) I need to get some sleep. What? Desert Storm. They say he was behind the Republican Guard's lines. Never came back.

Indio stands up, brushing off her pants. She smiles at Willie, starts down the hill.

> INDIO
> I'd *like* to see you tomorrow.

At the base of the knoll she waves to Willie and walks up an access road toward the trailers near the Wall of Death, when we see a single headlight appear over the rise at the edge of the campground. The headlight shudders as the battered RV bounces down the hill then turns onto the road. Indio looks over her shoulder, moves to the side of the road, and keeps walking as it rumbles toward her, springs squeaking, the silhouette of Pogo's broad brim hat behind the wheel. The RV leaps ahead, skidding broadside across the road in front of Indio as Whitey and Duke jump out. Duke shoves her to Whitey who sidearms her, knocking her down. Duke puts his foot on her neck, Whitey handcuffs her and they pull her into the RV.

INT.–RV–NIGHT

CLOSE:

A cardboard "deodorizer" in the shape of a naked woman dangling from the rearview mirror in the dim instrument panel lights, cigarette smoke drifting over it and the filthy windshield. We hear DUKE'S phoney, obscene LAUGH as the RV ROARS off, the cutout woman jerking with its acceleration.

WHITEY (OS)

You like *that?*

EXT.–AIRSTREAM–NIGHT

Glowing silver-orange from the bonfire across the camp where the Berserkers toast Shank at a huge, rough-hewn table. Cap steps INTO THE FRAME watching them, holding a liquor bottle by the neck. He brings it to his lips. Empty. He tries the door of the trailer. It opens.

INT.–AIRSTREAM–NIGHT

Very dark inside, suddenly illuminated as Cap opens the refrigerator, finds a beer, then closes the door, plunging the room into darkness again. We can barely see Cap where he leans against the refrigerator. We hear a SOUND. Someone crying? Then Bolten's muffled, angry voice.

CLOSE–CAP'S FACE, lined but handsome, even drunk, as he LISTENS to the muffled angry voice. Someone else crying.

> BOLTEN (OC)
> I'm not stopping *now.*

> GROUPIE #2 (OC)
> *Jenn*ifer. It's what you *wanted.*

Cap tiptoes drunkenly across the dark room toward the bedroom, past the dark shape of the aquarium, pausing.

CLOSE–CAP'S FACE, listening. Even drunk, the intelligence shows in his eyes. Suddenly they go wide at the faint WHISPER behind him.

> CUT TO:

The bedroom door. We can barely make it out. The WHISPER has turned to a sound like someone piling dead leaves.

> CAP(OC)
> *Praise* Jeezus. I *thought* I heard you little brothers
> and sisters.

We hear the unmistakable dry *rattle,* another, and Cap laughs. His voice grows louder.

> CAP (OC)
> The chosen, them that's been *chosen* now, can take
> up serpents.

The SOUND of snakes grows frantic and louder, rattling, boiling through the money, slapping the sides of the aquarium. Cap laughs louder, his voice LOUD now as we hold the bedroom door.

CAP (OC)
They can take up serpents, don't you see, and *command* them.

The bedroom door flies open, lighting the room, as Bolten LEAPS out, nunchucks in his hand, where he FREEZES. Off his LOOK, we pull back to show Cap, rattlers twined around his neck, coiling like ropes from his extended arms. Bolten slowly backs toward the bedroom door.

CAP
Chrome Wheels, right? Saw it in San Quentin.

Bolten SLAMS the door and we DISSOLVE TO:

Cap, stuffing money into a duffle bag, the snakes gliding around his arms each time he reaches in for an armful of bills. A single rattler is coiled in front of the bedroom door, his RATTLE rising and falling.
Cap tops off the duffle bag, hooks it closed, then picks up the single rattler and drops it back in the aquarium.

CAP
Wouldn't want anybody to step on you.

Outside, he straps the dufflebag on his bike with bungee cords, and rides away, unnoticed in the drunken celebration, the bonfire fading in the BG.

EXT.–BONFIRE–NIGHT

Women clear dishes from the massive table as the senior Berserkers listen to Voker and Shank.

VOKER
We're honored that you came up to see us, Shank.
We overlooked the fact that you came with a man

who renounced his colors. No problem. But we can't take every problem personally. They're after *Cap*, not you. It was just *business*. An accident they
. . . .

SHANK

They violated my home. Assaulted my *children*. I don't care who they were after.

VOKER

Be reasonable. For the first time, this club has some *money*. We paid a lot of dues. We can't risk all. . . .

SHANK

Thank you for the meal.

The Berserkers watch, hard-eyed, but we can see the mixed emotions in their faces.

VOKER

Stay the night at least, we'll. . . .

SHANK

Has anyone seen Cap?

The Berserkers shake their heads, then turn to look toward the sound of shouting.

BOLTEN (OC)

Snakes! Covered . . . with snakes.

EXT.–HIGHWAY–NIGHT

Cap pulling away from the campground–Home free!–Roaring through the gears, streaking down the highway, EXPLODING past a battered RV.

INT.–RV–NIGHT

                           POGO
That was *him.*

Through the windshield we see Cap's receding tail light. Duke is driving. Whitey walks up, adjusting his shirt.

                          WHITEY
"Him," who?
                           POGO
The guy. You know, the, uh, whadda you call it?
The *subject.*
                          WHITEY
Are you sure?
                           DUKE
It was him. The subject, all right.

                    WHITEY (ENRAGED)
Then go *after* him, goddammit. Punch it.

Duke floors the accelerator. The RV only drones at a slightly higher pitch.
                          WHITEY
Go! Don't . . . *lose* him.

As Cap's taillight vanishes in the distance, Whitey SMASHES the paneled wall. He PUNCHES the wall again, and the cabinet door above him FLIES open. The bug-eyed dead body of Petey, the dog that sings, his lips locked in a snarl, seems to spring out, hitting Whitey in the chest.

EXT.–HIGHWAY–NIGHT

Cap slows the bike, smile fading. He downshifts, pulls to the shoulder, and looks back at the glow of the Berserker's bonfire high above Sturgis. He looks at the dufflebag. Resigned, without joy, he pulls back onto the freeway. He tops a hill and there below him, illuminated by spotlights, the big American flag curls above thousands of white tombstones.

EXT.–CEMETERY–NIGHT

Cap stuffs bills into the donations box. More. He looks in the bag, hesitates, the big flag ringing above him against the flagpole, then dumps in all the rest.

                    CAP
     That should buy you a few senators.
                    CUT TO:

Cap, on his back beneath a bulldozer, opening the drain valve. He jerks his head back as diesel pours out.

EXT.–HIGHWAY–NIGHT

The battered RV rolls down a deserted highway.

              WHITEY (OC)
     Pogo. Leave her alone for a while, OK? He's up
     the road somewhere.

EXT.–EDGE OF CEMETERY–NIGHT

A steaming lake of diesel fuel spreads beneath all the earth moving equipment. A narrow stream of it trickles back, back, to where Cap stands holding a gas can. He sets the can down, looks back at the rows of grave markers glowing in the moonlight, thumbs a flame onto his Marine Corps Zippo. CLOSE as it falls from his hand.

INT.–RV–NIGHT
Pogo making his way to the front of the RV when a HUGE explosion and fireball just off the highway rocks the vehicle, THROWS Pogo against the wall.

EXT.–EDGE OF CEMETERY–NIGHT

Cap sits with his back to a tombstone, watching the ROARING, deafening blaze. A gas tank EXPLODES, cartwheeling a backhoe as we see movement in the tombstones behind Cap. People slipping from stone to stone.

EXT.–CEMETERY–DAY

Shank and Willie stand next to Cap's bike, looking at the smoking wreckage of heavy equipment.

> OLD LADY (OC)
> Terrible, isn't it?

They turn to see the woman who works at the administration building. She doesn't *really* think it's "terrible."

> OLD LADY
> Where's your friend? You know, I felt bad for him
> yesterday. I *knew* he wanted to contribute. Tell him
> that a wonderful thing happened. When I came in
> this morning, the donation box was *full.* Hundred
> dollar bills. . . .
> SHANK
> Did you see him?

> OLD LADY
> Your friend? The only people I've seen today were
> retirees. And an old RV driving off when I got here.
> All beat up. (smiles) Covered with flags.

EXT.–DESERT ROAD–DAY

A patched stretch of blacktop through ugly desert. Buzzards wheel in the cloudless, unforgiving sky as a coyote peels a piece of roadkill

192

off the pavement. We hear the WHINE of a vehicle. The coyote trots off the road and watches from a ditch as the RV whistles past. A cigarette flies out the window, exploding in sparks on the pavement.

INT.–RV–DAY

Cap, badly beaten, is handcuffed to the kitchen sink. He opens his swollen eyes when Pogo's shadow falls over him.

> POGO
>
> He's not hurt so bad.

> CAP
>
> Who are you people?

> WHITEY (OC)
>
> Tell him.

> POGO
>
> Operatives. DEA. Drug Enforcement Admini-stration.

> CAP
>
> You've spent more time in the joint than on the street. Got that shuffle snitches and informants have from being locked-down in isolation. Three and a half steps across the cell, three and a half back. . . .

Pogo picks up a fancy white leather-bound Bible the size of the L.A. *Yellow Pages,* and slams Cap's head, two-handed. Again. Puts the blood-smeared Bible on the stove and walks away.

> INDIO (OC)
>
> Don't give them an excuse to hurt you. I'll need your help.

Cap twists around to see Indio, beaten and half-naked, handcuffed to the bed. Up front, Duke *whoops.*

> DUKE
> Shit *fire!* Dee-Eee-*A.* The elite.

INT.–DEA OFFICE–DAY

At his desk, McCoy field strips an Army .45, cleaning it while Durham paces the room.

> DURHAM
> I'm not some kind of dope pusher. My conscience
> is clear on utilizing cocaine seizures to fund my
> operation.

McCoy holds the .45 barrel up, squints through it.

> MCCOY
> *Theoretically* speaking. No one would really do that.
> Being it's a *felony,* and everything. . . .

> DURHAM
> This war–on drugs–uses tactics just like any other
> deadly conflict. It's really a war against these
> third-world countries draining our economy. . . .

> CUT TO:

Calloused hands thumbing through a battered copy of Chairman Mao's "little red book." The *swish* of a tissue-thin page being turned to some phrase. HOLD on the book, the thumb pausing as we hear

DURHAM (OC)

Against these two-bit terrorists. We need money to fight that war. If we have to sell cocaine to inner-city crackheads to get it, so what? They're beyond saving. At least their money is doing some good for a change. Financing our operations. It's morally *impeccable.*

MCCOY

(Laughs)I wouldn't go that far, (beat) theoretically speaking.

The HANDS close the book and we CUT TO:

McCoy reassembling the .45. His hands much like those with the book, only lighter-skinned.

MCCOY

Whatever works.

He attaches the slide, cocks it, dry fires it. Puts a full magazine in, chambers a round, and thumbs the safety on.

MCCOY

Damn fine weapon. I don't know *why* they want to change to the Beretta. *Who'd* buy a gun from an *Italian. . .* ?

The phone rings and Durham picks it up, listens, rolls his eyes at McCoy.

DURHAM

Put 'em through. . . . That's confirmed? Excellent work. Transport the subject to this location. Roger that.

He hangs up.

MCCOY

Roger dodger, over and out. What was *that* about?

DURHAM

My "operatives." Whitey, Pogo, and Duke. The
Duke of Paducah.

MCCOY

I don't like dealing with scum like that. You never
know what they might. do. They *lie* . . . you promised them jobs?

DURHAM

I'll give them a badge and fly 'em down to Bogota.
They picked up that guy who was in the cell with
Kolchek.

MCCOY

Carter Kolchek wouldn't have said anything. I used
to work with him. Good man. They didn't have to
call him a faggot. . . .

DURHAM

Nothing beats being certain.

INT.–RV–DAY

Cap has twisted around so he can talk to Indio. The RV stopped
on the side of the road.

CAP

. . . this plumbing will pull right out of the wall.

INDIO

Pogo wears his handcuff key around his neck on a
(beat) long, *dirty* string. I've seen it.

Through the little window above Cap's head we see Whitey hang
up the roadside phone. When he says something to the other two
they *whoop*, giving each other high-fives as they walk around to
the door.

CAP

You hang in there. I'll try to take a little of the heat
off you.

Pogo does a little dance to the back of the RV where he looks down at Indio.

> POGO
> I feel good. Elite. Ready for action. (to Cap) I'll let you watch, *duuude.*
> CAP
> You move like a jailhouse faggot.

Pogo looks at him. Looks at Indio. Smiles.

> POGO
> Whatever.

As he steps back, sets himself, *snaps* a jab into Cap's face.

EXT.–GAS STATION–DAY:

At the edge of an expensive new shopping district where the wives of rich men spend their mornings. Rodeo Drive with a Southwest flavor, palm trees lining the street. A good-looking young attendant smiles and waves at a woman driving a Rolls as she pulls away from the pump. As he watches her drive off we hear the CLATTER of an engine with a bad spark plug. The attendant frowns and turns to see:
The RV shuddering its way to the pumps, blowing black smOKe, more beatup than ever. He walks to the RV, a look of distaste and contempt on his face. His expression freezes as the filthy window slides open and Pogo looks down at him.

> POGO
> Fill it up, kid.
> ATTENDANT
> Regular?
> POGO
> You stupid? Vehicle like this takes Hi-test. Get that windshield, too.

Pogo opens the squeaking door as Whitey and Duke get out of the back, Whitey's arm around a bruised and gaunt-eyed Indio.

> WHITEY
> Where's your shitter at? My fee-yon-say here. . . .

DUKE laughs.

> WHITEY (CONT)
> . . . needs to relieve herself.   CUT TO:

The attendant hangs up the nozzle, then stuffs the rag they use as a gas cap into the filler hole. Whitey walks Indio back to the RV as Duke and Pogo come out of the station, their arms full of beer, potato chips, jerky. The manager of the place steps out the door and calls to the attendant.

> MANAGER
> Rick. Add in the price of that stuff.

INT.–RV–DAY

As Whitey cuffs Indio to the bed, he looks down at a bloody, unconscious Cap. He goes to the front, dumps the ashtray out the window, then kicks a clutter of beer cans and fast-food trash out as he climbs back out.

> WHITEY
> What do I owe you for the gas, kid?

> ATTENDANT
> Well, I'll have to add in the beer. . . .

> WHITEY
> I said, how much for the gas.

> ATTENDANT
> Gas comes to . . . twenty-six fifty.

WH ITEY
Say what?

ATTENDANT
Twenty-six. . . .

Whitey walks up and gets in the kid's face.

WHITEY (HISSING)
You trying to fuck me, kid?

ATTENDANT.
Sir?

WHITEY
I said, you trying to fuck me? How much you
bastards trying to charge for gas?

The terrified kid looks over at the clearly posted prices.

WHITEY
Look at *me,* boy. I'm talking to you. You better show
me some *respect.* You people think you're better than
us?

He grabs a handful of the kid's cheek, looks over his shoulder at
Pogo . . .

WHITEY
Pogo, let's go get some money.

. . . and walks the kid, crying in pain, toward the office.

WHITEY
Come on, pretty cheeks. Pretty Peaches.

They walk into the office/snack store, Pogo following with an old
long-barreled .38 in his hand. The manager just stands there,

watching them, not quite believing what he sees as Whitey pulls the knife from his belt and, without breaking stride, drives it into the manager's chest. Again. The manager stumbles, throws up one arm, as Whitey strikes *down* now, the manager falling. Music plays in the garage area.

> WHITEY
>
> Add in the price of *that*, fucker. Nobody fucks me. I don't. *Take. Shit.*

Whitey shoves the kid into the cash register.

> WHITEY
>
> Open it.

He does, and Whitey grabs him and shoves him to Pogo.

> WHITEY
>
> Take him. See who's in the damn garage.

We hear the music more clearly now as Pogo and the kid walk into the garage where a radio plays. The legs and work boots of a mechanic stick out from beneath a car held up by a floor jack. Pogo walks to the jack. . . .

> MECHANIC'S VOICE
>
> Sir, you'll have to wait in the office. Our insurance company won't. . . .

. . . and flips the release, dropping the car down on him, then looks at the kid, digging in one ear with a dirty finger.

> DUKE
>
> Peaches and cream, huh? Get over to that work bench. (beat) You better *move.*

As Pogo follows behind him, we

CUT TO:
INT.–RV–DAY

As Cap RIPS the plumbing out of the wall, water gushing out.

INT.–OFFICE–DAY

Whitey dumps the cash register tray on the floor as Duke walks in. We can see the RV through the window, water pouring through the frame in sheets.
                        DUKE
        What's going on?

                        WHITEY
        What does it look like? You're supposed to be
        watching the prisoners. Get back to your post.

When Duke climbs back into the RV, on the far side, Cap rises up behind him and uses his handcuff chain like a garotte, choking him out, dragging him back through the water to Indio who pulls the handcuff key off.

INT.–GAS STATION OFFICE–DAY

Whitey looks up and sees Indio fall by the front of the RV. She gets up and stumbles toward the street.

                        WHITEY
        God damn. Go get her. Pogo!

CLOSE: the radio playing music.

                        WHITEY (OS)
        Pogo!
                        POGO (OS)
        All right, goddammit. Shit.

201

We hear a *thud.* Again. Then the sound of something metal hitting concrete.

EXT.–GAS STATION–DAY

As Whitey runs past the front of the RV, Cap steps out and hits him in the face with the kitchen faucets, knocking him down. He sees Pogo going after Indio and trys to intercept him, weak and limping badly.

CAP

Run!

But Pogo catches her. Cap is about to swing the plumbing down on Pogo when we hear a GUNSHOT. ANOTHER. Cap turns, drops the faucet, tries to sit down, but falls instead. Duke, soaking wet, his face red, brings up his TEC-9 to fire again. Pogo, standing in the line of fire, yells

POGO

No! Stop! Hold your fire!

Traffic has stopped–executives going to the office, women in station wagons taking kids to school, Mexicans in pickups, all watching. Whitey suddenly realizes this.

WHITEY

Let's get the fuck out of here!

They get in and lurch off, smashing parked cars out of the way .

EXT.–STREET–DAY

The RV rockets out of town, traffic jamming up behind it, keeping a patrol car from getting through.

INT.–RV–DAY

At the sound of a siren, Duke shoves Indio into the bathroom and locks the door. Whitey looks back at a motorcycle cop behind them. He staggers to the ruined sink, hanging against the rocking RV, shouts to Pogo who is driving.

                    WHITEY
        Keep going. It's just one guy.

A string of EXPLOSIONS rocks the RV, scaring hell out of both of them, deafening them, flying glass cutting Whitey's face. As Pogo fights to get control of the RV again,

                                        CUT TO:

DUKE holding a smoking TEC-9, looking out what's left of the back window, grinning. Whitey slugs him, shouts.

                    WHITEY
        What the hell's wrong with you?

                    DUKE
        He's gone.

                    WHITEY
        What?

              DUKE (SHOUTING)
        I said THE FUCKER'S GONE!

                    WHITEY
        WHAT?

ENT.–GAS STATION–DAY

Late afternoon, the gas station webbed with yellow police tape, Shank and Willie talking to a detective.

EXT.–STREET

Willie and Shank walking out of the coroner's office. Shank slaps Willie on the shoulder and points toward the desert. They start their bikes, ride off, Willie on Cap's Harley.

EXT.–DESERT–NIGHT

A campfire glows next to the RV. A BULLET explodes sparks from it and we HEAR Duke's phoney LAUGH.

> POGO (OS)
> What's so *funny,* man?

Three more bullets explode into the fire and we
>> CUT TO:

Duke as he turns from the fire and points his TEC-9 pistol at Pogo, clicking the safety on and off, laughing.

> POGO
> You retard. You probably cost us our jobs when you killed our man. I'll shove that thing up your ass.
> DUKE
> What were you shovin' back at the station, you jail-house faggot? I heard what that guy Cap called you.
> WHITEY
> Both of you shut up.
> DUKE
> What are we hangin' around in the fuckin' desert for? We got money for a motel.

Whitey has the shotgun slung across his back on a rope.

WHITEY

We're staying low-profile till we get to the air strip.
I don't know where else we can go.

DUKE

Oh, *man*. I hate camping. There's scary shit out
there in the dark, man.

WHITEY

Quit whining. I'm trying to think here.

He looks at Indio, sprawled by the car. He crouches, stands up,
opening and closing a mean-looking folding knife.

CUT TO:

POV SHOT: From out in the dark we see the RV and campfire
in the distance. PULL BACK to Shank and Willie–watching, the
Harleys rumbling softly, Shank pulls his shotgun from its scab-
bard and hands it to Willie. Willie shakes his head, but Shank
FORCES it on him, pantomiming how to pump and fire it.

DUKE (OS)

Think about what? Her? She's all wore out.

CLOSE: Indio's face. Her eyes are open but barely alive.

We HEAR bikes out in the dark, winding up, going through the
gears. Indio hears them too. Her eyes show more life.

CUT TO:

DUKE, squinting into the dark.

DUKE

. . . the fuck is that?

As the bikes get louder, closer, Whitey and Pogo have already scrambled into the RV.

A puff of wind seems to tug Duke's shirtsleeve. He looks down just as the report of Shank's .45 reaches him and blood blossoms on the fabric. As Shank and Willie BLAST out of the dark, the RV lurches backwards, then fishtails forward, screening Duke from them. Willie manages to ride around the RV, but Shank has to lay his bike down in a cloud of dust as the RV drives on. Shank raises up, finds his .45, then, through the dust, sees Duke with the TEC-9 to Indio's head.

> DUKE
> Put the gun down and get over by the fire. Did you *see* that? They *left* me. I *hate* camping, man. I'll shoot her. Get over there.

He backs into the shadows of yucca trees, shoves Indio to her knees, and aims at Shank. For just an instant, a long second, his face seems spotlighted, surprised, cutting his eyes toward the yucca. Then it vanishes in the reddish yellow MUZZLE BLAST from less than two feet away. Willie steps out from the yucca, holding the shotgun on the decapitated Duke.

CLOSE–WILLIE'S FACE

> DISSOLVE TO:

EXT.–DESERT–DAWN

CLOSE: WILLIE'S FACE as he and Shank, prone in the sand, study the ghost town/air strip in the distance just as the sun comes up. The first light eats shadows in the ghost town, glints off the windshield of the filthy RV.

> SHANK
> Security guards. Lots of them. They look pretty sharp, too. Leave the shotgun and take her some-where safe. I've got food and water for a couple

206

days if need be. All I can do is wait. I'll see you
when you get back.

EXT.–MAPLE MOTOR COURT–DAY

Two rows of adobe motel units around a courtyard and fountain.
Willie's bike parked in front of the rearmost unit. As we watch, he
backs out the door, closes it gently, then rolls his Harley to the
road before starting it. He looks back the way he came, then skids
the bike around and rides off the other way, rocketing out of sight.

INT.–AIRSTREAM–NIGHT

Two *new* groupies dropping mice into the snake aquarium. A knock
on the door and K-mart sticks his head in.

> K-MART
> Boss? Stafford's here.

Voker nods and Stafford comes in, does a double-take at the mostly
naked groupies, then tries to act cool. He wears a very expensive
3-piece suit and blue-tinted sunglasses.

> VOKER (TO GROUPIES)
> Why don't you girls take a break? My rattlesnakes
> are getting fat. Go do some drugs or something.

At this Bolten shouts from the bedroom.

> BOLTEN (OC)
> Send 'em in here.

As they go, Voker looks at Stafford.

VOKER

The papers are calling me scum, man. What about
this indictment thing? You said they didn't have
enough evidence to. . . .

K-MART (OC)

Don't we have any *diet* Cokes?

STAFFORD

It's just a grand jury. A waste of the state's time and
money. . . .

VOKER

My time and money, too. What about *my* time?

K-MART (OC)

Regular, Classic, whatever the fuck it's called, but
no fuckin' *diet* Cokes. I don't need the sugar, man.

One of the girls in the bedroom SHRIEKS.

VOKER

K-Mart, it's a time and place for every damn thing,
and right now I'm trying to keep my ass out of jail.

As the two groupies come out of the bedroom wearing leather
chaps and cowboy hats, Bolten stands behind them, grinning as
they call to Voker in unison, drawing his name out.

GROUPIES

Oh, Voooh-ker the Joooh-ker. We're ready to ride.

STAFFORD

I guess this is as good a time as any to tell you to
expect an IRS audit. I faxed your old returns. . . .

VOKER

Give 'em money. Take care of it. Whatever works.
I gotta get out of here.

Stafford calls to him as he walks away, and Voker turns, points his finger at the lawyer.

VOKER

You better keep me out of jail.

They all watch in silence as he goes out the door.

EXT.–CAMP–NIGHT

Voker sits on a boulder where the road begins to curve downhill to the campground where they are dismantling the booths and rides. A single headlight breaks away from the lights below, winding up the road till it stops at the boulder. It's Willie. Voker looks down, expressionless.

VOKER

What do *you* want, kid? You're lucky I don't shoot
you. Your old man stole over a quarter million of
my dollars.

WILLIE

Cap's dead.

VOKER

Well . . . I'm sorry. Even though he *stole* from me.
Sorry.

WILLIE

The people who killed him are hiding out in some
sort of camp south of here. I've got a map. . . .

VOKER

What do I care, kid? Cap's already dead, so cut
your losses. Go home.

                    WILLIE
Shank's waiting for me. He probably thinks I ran
away. I left him on my own to ask for your help. I
shouldn't have come.

                    VOKER
Go home, kid. While you still have a future.

Willie tosses the map down, turns his bike and looks up. Voker
looks like a lizard on the boulder.

                    WILLIE
My dad always liked you. Even after he got out of
prison. But he said you thought too much.

Voker watches him ride down the hill until he loses him in the
other lights, then slides off the boulder and walks toward the
glowing Airstream.
                    VOKER
OK , what?
                    K-MART
Cap had a pretty good kid. I heard about him
standing up to Mickey down at Gunnar's lounge.

Voker keeps walking, hands in pockets, not looking back.

                    VOKER
I got troubles of my own, K-Mart.

                    K-MART
Sure. Goodnight, boss. (beat) I picked up his map
if you. . . .
                    VOKER
No.

INT.–AIRSTREAM–NIGHT

Voker sits alone. It's late. The only light is from a trac-light illuminating the aquarium. Voker walks to the aquarium, bends down and watches the snakes swimming in money. A mouse skeleton appears and vanishes in waves of green bills.

SNAKE'S POV

Voker peering in. He taps the glass. A snake strikes at him. Another. More, until we can barely make out his face through the coiling, striking rattlers.

EXT.–CAMP–NIGHT

Voker walks through the camp, Berserkers passed out, sick, groaning in their sleep. The bonfire is dying. Bad Bill's old lady is giving him a hard time in their tent.

> BAD BILL'S OLD LADY (OC)
> . . . because we *need* more room. You deserve a better house. And so do *I*. Well, *don't* I?

EXT.–AIRSTREAM DOOR–NIGHT

As rattlesnakes wind to the threshold, look into the night, their tongues tasting the air. The heavy snakes slide off, hitting the ground with *thuds*, one or two at first, then in swarms, pouring out the door.

> VOKER
> You're gonna have to find your own mice from now on.

The snakes swarming around his ankles, brushing up against his legs like fawning cats.

> DISSOLVE TO:

EXT.–CAMPGROUND–NIGHT (NO SOUND)

It's almost dawn as the Berserkers wait on their bikes in a loose half-circle, passing a couple bottles of Jim Beam. The firelight reflecting off their bikes gets brighter. It looks like a silent dream. PAN along the column of bikers, the crank whores with them. We see the barrel of a sawed-off shotgun glint just below the edge of a denim vest. A macheté. The taped-up grip of an old .38 sticking out of a boot. A Chevy van, dented and primered in spots, and a beat-up flatbed truck with a winch on the bed, bring up the rear. A bumper sticker on the side of the truck reads, "HUGS NOT DRUGS."

We HEAR the ROARING flames, and beneath that the idling bikes, then Voker as he SHOUTS

VOKER (OC)
Does anybody here want to live forever?

REVERSE ANGLE

Voker stands in front of the flaming Airstream, the flames feeding on MONEY, singed and burning bills boiling up into the night sky. He raises his hands over his head and the gang cheers.

THE GANG
No! *Hell* no! Nobody lives forever!

Voker walks to his bike, saddlebags over his shoulder.

VOKER
Well then, I think it's time we went there in the
world and cut us a little payback. Took back a little
of what's ours. What do you think? Can we make
a *difference* out there?

They kick their bikes into life, the roar echoing off the canyon walls, black exhaust fouling the air.

THE GANG
Let's *do* it. Let's party. Let's *kick some ass!*

Voker looks at the Airstream, then at the gang.

VOKER
Then let's get into that black wind out there!

The ROAR of bikes blasts the screen BLACK.

EXT.–CAMP–DAWN

The AIRSTREAM still burning, dripping molten aluminum.

CLOSE: A single coiled rattler, his scales gleaming in the light from the flames.

EXT.–HIGHWAY–DAY

A few cars pass by. A tractor-trailer.
CUT TO:

EXT.–HIGHWAY–AFTERNOON

Another stretch of highway. A big electric sign up ahead announces:
CALIFORNIA HIGHWAY FATALITIES TO DATE
BUCKLE UP
Beneath this are foot-high lighted numbers, in the thousands now, that increase every few hours or days to reflect the statistics.

HOLD ON THE SIGN.

A couple of cars go past. A VW van. A truck.

HOLD ON THE SIGN.

As the number increases by one. We hear something now. It sounds like motorcycles.
Yes, it *is* motorcycles. Lots of them. Getting louder.
The sign increases by one more . . . two . . . threefour.
The roar of the bikes gets louder and closer and the sign increases by onetwo . . . threefourfive . . .
And the BERSERKERS EXPLODE THROUGH THE FRAME and the numbers on the sign blink and twitch and add up like the fractions of gallons on a high-volume gas pump.

SERIES OF SHOTS:

Voker and K-Mart leading the pack of Berserkers down the freeway, up the center line, feeding into the crush of automobiles.
The two of them, side-by-side behind a Volvo station wagon. A bumper sticker reads: _____. Two white-bread little boys watch them over the back seat, their eyes wide. One of them gives a shy little wave, and K-Mart salutes him just as traffic opens up, and the whole club goes around the Volvo.

EXT.–GAS STATION–DAY:

A couple of Bandidos lay back on their chopped bikes watching freeway traffic. One of them is LESTER.

                    LESTER
          Mileage update, Moe. Bumfuck California to El
          Paso, Texas. *My* home town.

                    MOE
          Eight-hundred, forty-seven miles. If we don't sleep,
          we should. . . .

As Voker and Bad Bill roar past, followed by the rest of the club.

MOE

Fuckin' Berserkers, man. Hey! I heard . . . a run
down south. Something about Shank.

LESTER

Well, let's see if they can use any help. Sleep. Sleep?
(laughs) We'll sleep when we're dead.

They throw half-empty beer cans aside and crank up their bikes.

EXT.–FREEWAY–DAY

More bikes than before, not just Berserkers, people from a number
of clubs.

CUT TO:

VOKER and WILLIE, cutting through traffic, up the center line,
passing a new BMW, their colors flashing past–*whap whap*.

CUT TO:

The driver of the BMW, watching them out the windshield as
they thread their way through traffic and the rest of the bikers go
around him on both sides. The driver is a nice-looking young guy
who's worked in an office ever since he got out of college. HOLD
on his face as the bikes ROAR past–how he wishes *he* was on one
of them.

CUT TO:

EXT.–CROSSROADS–DAY

A dusty rural crossroads where a kid pumps gas into a pickup at
an old gas station as a formation of HUNS MC comes to a stop at
the flashing red light and looks up the other road to where a group
of BROTHER SPEED MC approaches in a cloud of dust. The
BROTHER SPEED group stops at the light, and the two groups

sit there, idling, revving their bikes, looking hard at each other. There's bad blood between them. The Hun's Road Captain shouts over the roar to the Brother Speed leader.

> HUNS ROAD CAPTAIN
> We'll settle it another time.

The Brother Speed leader looks back at his men to see how they want to handle it, then nods to the Hun's Road Captain. The two groups merge and thunder together down the road.

EXT.–DESERT–NIGHT

Shank checks his shotgun, the .45, extra clips of ammo. He's smeared his face with bark. A few lights twinkle in the ghost town. He's ready to go when he hears something behind him and waits. It's Willie, on foot.

> SHANK
> I thought you'd gone back to your mom.

> WILLIE
> I managed to get a little help.

Willie looks at his watch and we hear the first distant roar, like a faraway ocean. It grows and gets louder and out of the dark, to the left of the town, we see the first Molotov cocktails floating through the night like spirits, burning blue and green.

They get closer, closer, and a few shots are fired from the ghost town. The bikes turn on their headlights now, in formation, the blazing headlights eating up the dark desert between them and the town when more fire comes. A biker's headlight goes black in a burst of sparks.

A burst of green tracers arcs from the town. A bike goes down, then another one, its own Molotov cocktail EXPLODING in flames.

The bikes, still in formation, turn just in front of the security fence, tossing the cocktails, then turning off their headlights, riding off in all directions. Two of the buildings are in flames. We see a SECONDARY EXPLOSION–AMMUNITION.
The headlights of another phalanx of bikes flare on, coming down on the town from the north.

DISSOLVE TO:

EXT.–GHOST TOWN–NIGHT

As headlights turn onto the street with a roar of bikes, the men with guns start shooting. Muzzle flashes blink from the bikes as they keep coming, ROAR PAST, the Rangers blowing some of the riders off their bikes.

EXT.–DEA COMMO CENTER–NIGHT

Jittery Rangers out front. Shooting in the background. Buildings down the street are on fire. McCoy comes out the door and looks around. Speaks to the Rangers in Spanish, claps them on the shoulders.

MCCOY (IN SPANISH–SUBTITLES)
All because of that scum he hired. Hiding in there.

He indicates the commo center, then turns and walks down the street, his .45 in his hand.

CUT TO:

Shank, K-mart, Voker, Willie and a handful of the others (the HUN's leader, Mickey, and the two Bandidos) watching this from an alley just up the street. Shank loads his model 12. He has a couple extra clips for the .45 in his belt. He and Voker are pretty shot up. Shank has *three* wound bandannas on his legs and arm. Shank points to a bloody patch on Voker's side, along the short ribs.

SHANK

How's that one? Bad?

VOKER

Not so bad.

SHANK

It must *hurt* like a son-of-a-bitch.

VOKER

Hell no, it doesn't hurt.

Voker winces when he says this, and all of them almost laugh out loud. Shank looks around the corner of the building, down the street, then back at the others. Dresser Jim's fancy outfit is torn and dirty, a bloodstain down one arm.

SHANK

This is what we came for. How do you want to do it?

VOKER

Head on. Shooting.

LESTER

Might as well.

SHANK

That always worked for us.

They adjust their guns and stand stiffly up.

DRESSER JIM

He's sure got a lot of bodyguards.

SHANK

Those guys usually lose their enthusiasm pretty fast.

                    VOKER
I could never figure out that bodyguard stuff.
Expecting somebody to step in front of a bullet for
a paycheck. Hell, does that make sense to *you?*

They look at each other and almost smile.

                    SHANK
    Let's go.

They step out of the shadows walking and limping toward the
commo center.
                    VOKER
    Boy-Howdy. This'll be one for the books, won't it?

                    SHANK
    Remember that time up in Oakland. . . .

                    K-MART
    When the Huns thought they'd move in on us?

                    HUN'S LEADER
    I was there.

Shank turns and looks at him, at all of them.

                    SHANK
    Hell, we were all just kids then.

They all start to laugh as they walk toward the guards.

                    GUARD
    Hey. . . .

The bikers start shooting, their muzzle blasts flaring in the fog.
They walk steadily, side-by-side, firing and jacking in fresh rounds

as they go. The guards' pistols blink as they try to get off a few shots–rounds *snap* past the bikers–but the guards have been taken by surprise, overwhelmed by the shotguns, and they go down.

Shank aims the shotgun just a *second* longer as one of the guards turns to run, then fires. The guard only manages a couple of steps, not even striding yet, when his legs go out from under him, and the buckshot slaps him down onto the street.

At the door to the commo center, one of the fallen guards rolls over and the HUN puts another pattern of shot into him, his last round. He drops the shotgun and pulls out a two inch model 29, as Shank chambers a solid slug in his shotgun and blows the door open.

LESTER

We wouldn't have made El Paso tonight anyway.

As Shank drops *his* now empty shotgun and pulls his .45, Willie crosses in front of him, and they go through the door. Inside, Whitey and Pogo, almost in shock, bring their guns up.

DISSOLVE TO:

EXT.–DESERT–NIGHT

In the distance, the ghost town is in flames. MCCOY'S private plane takes off and heads south as the bikers pull out of the ruined town and begin to regroup.

Then we hear a shudder in the air. Most of these guys know the sound of a Huey gunship when they hear it. They listen, smell the wind, look for it as the rotors get louder. Check their guns. They've got nowhere to hide.

Then the chopper is on them, the cherry red glow of the jet turbine flickering on the rotor blades as it POUNDS OVERHEAD in a reconnaissance pass. The bikers watch it wheel around, come back, the door gunners on each side stitching red M-60 tracers down through the bikers, their pistols and rifles not much good against it as it carves a path of death, roars past, then wheels again for another pass.

220

Then we HEAR a little gasoline engine out in the dark. A very distinctive sound, one we've heard before. The generator Tiny was working on.

As the gunship begins its next pass a bolt of red fire blazes up from the sound of the generator that powers a mini-gun bolted to the back of Tiny's 3-wheeler. The red bolt hangs in the sky like a bloody searchlight, traversing, looking for the gunship.

Tiny cranks the gun with a series of gears, the muzzle blast from the thousand-round-a-minute gun blowing his clothes and hair and beard like an apocolyptic wind. He looks like Moses parting the Red Sea.

The red bolt of light finds the Huey, touches it, and the chopper explodes above the burning town, flaming wreckage adding to the fire.

EXT.–MAPLE MOTOR COURT–DAY

Willie and Indio strap packs on their bikes, fire them up, and ride south on the blacktop road.

PULL BACK TO REVEAL

Shank and Tiny, watching them go.

DISSOLVE TO:

EXT.–ROAD–DAY:

The sound and lighting give the following the quality of a dream or a memory.

Willie riding down a pretty stretch of road, trees reaching out over the blacktop, dappling it with shade. He glances in his rearview mirror as we hear the sound of another bike. Indio pulls INTO THE FRAME and matches her speed to his.

Willie and Indio downshift as the highway funnels them into a small town, past speed limit signs. They pass a patrol car half-hidden in some trees, a cop wearing sunglasses aiming a radar gun at them.

They cruise through the little magic-mile main street of town, past the fast-food joints, used car lots and video stores, and out the other end where we see a fenced-in elemetary school playground full of kids. One of the kids accidentally kicks a soccer ball over the fence, and it bounces onto the road in front of the two bikes. They downshift and stop, their bikes growling, and Willie picks up the ball as the kids swarm to the fence. They look almost like prisoners there, their fingers gripping the chain-links, as Willie tosses the ball back to them.

KID #1

Thanks, mister.

KID #2

Those are great bikes. Where are you guys going?

Willie looks at Indio, then back at the kid.

WILLIE

I think we'll go down to Mexico—where the palm trees grow. (beat) But we'll be back.

The kid gives Willie a "thumbs up" and Willie returns it.

WILLIE

Good luck, kid.

Willie and Indio roll slowly down the street, past School Zone speed limit signs as the kids run along the fence as far as they can, watching them. Willie glances back at them, then looks at Indio, smiles.

They accelerate, ride off down the road as "Cap's song" begins to play.

Outtakes from
Sympathy for the Devil
(1980-81)

1

H anson woke up as the band of sunlight touched his cheek and moved across his eyes. He opened his eyes and lay still. For a moment he didn't know where he was. The ceiling, walls, and floor of the bedroom were all painted baby blue. The only furniture in the room was an old wood and wicker wheelchair painted the same color as the room. A large poster of Che Guevera was tacked to the opposite wall. He was wearing a black beret with a red star on the front. He was looking directly down at Hanson, and seemed to be brooding. *"Que pasó, Che?"* Hanson asked.

Hanson glanced at the other side of the bed. It was empty, but there were red and purple stains on the sheets. He touched his finger to his cheek, then looked at it. It was bright red. A radio was playing in another room, " . . . do you believe in magic, yeah, does it make you feel groovy like an old-time movie. . . . "

Hanson pulled on his bluejeans and tennis shoes, then slipped a black tee-shirt over his shoulder-length blond hair. He took the stairs two at a time.

Betty was sitting at the kitchen table drinking Chinese herb tea with Carla. Carla was a chunky woman wearing green coveralls with the words "SUN COAL" across the back, and "Fred" stitched over the breast pocket. Her hair was pulled back in a bun, and she was wearing black combat boots. Her striped overall pants had a sewn-in hammer loop and nail apron. She turned her head slowly, and looked at Hanson. Staring at him, she spoke to Betty, "You have strange taste in men."

"You look like a real worker, Carla. On your way down to punch in at the plant?"

Carla ignored him.

Hanson picked up Carla's cup, and looked inside it, "Yuk. Commie tea. Wait. The leaves say . . . " He swirled the tea around, " . . . there is no god but God, and Mohammed is his prophet."

Carla's hand shot out toward his crotch, but he blocked it easily. "Better take a couple more of those karate lessons, Carla."

Betty was sitting in an overstuffed chair, her legs tucked beneath her. She was a handsome woman. Her long black hair was done up in braids. Her complexion was olive, and she could have passed for an Indian, an Arab, a Jew, a Mexican, almost any minority or third-world citizen. Her father was a psychiatrist, and her mother was a buyer for Saks 5th Avenue.

Hanson walked over to a revolving wire bookrack that was stocked with radical pamphlets and anti-war newspapers. The papers were cheap gray newsprint, and the photo reproductions were poor, some of them little more than black and gray smudges with captions like, "Chicago pigs attack peaceful demonstration." It could have been a photo of a car wreck in a storm. One photograph had the wrong caption. A glowering Cuban in a beret was captioned, "New York delegates sign resolution."

"Hey, Betty," Hanson asked, "How come you handle this bullshit?"

224

"Because I believe in it. And I do what I can. I'd rather be like me than like you, full of energy, angry at the same things I am, but with nowhere to go. You're like a walking bomb. Like last night. . . . "

"I think that's enough Psychology 101. . . . "

" . . . like last night. What was the paint for?"

"See what people would do. Most of 'em pretended not to see me. Like I was invisible. I read somewhere that people who are crippled or disfigured go crazy sometimes 'cause they start thinking that they're invisible. People on the street won't look at them. They don't want to see anything that's ugly. It scares them."

"Why do you want to scare people? Half the people at that party tried to stay in another room from you."

"All the bright liberals patting each other on the back. Hey, I'm against the fuckin' war, I'm against poverty, and racism, and disease, and tornados. So what? See, I'm scared. I like to spread it around some. Like academic arguments where I just imply, 'I may be wrong, but I can kick your ass.' I always win.

"Well," he said, "I'll leave you ladies here to manage the revolution. I'm going to go join the army."

Carla rolled her eyes.

The air piston on the screen door hissed slowly closed behind him.

Hanson bounced across the street to his battered black Chevrolet.

"Good morning, Jerome," he said, patting the rusty fender, "what a day, huh? Look at that sky, it just goes on and on and gets bluer."

The sunlight swung onto Hanson as he turned to get into the car, glancing off his heavy brass shooting-star belt buckle.

For an instant, when it first caught the sun, the star seemed to leap, but it was only a quick gold flash of light.

On the way across town, Hanson passed the courthouse. There was a big demonstration going on. Hanson drove around the block and parked the car. He got out, and stiff-armed the hinge-sprung door closed.

"Gonna let you sit here and air out a little, Jerome," he said. The Chevrolet was still rocking on its worn suspension when Hanson pivoted to cross the street. "Yes, yes, yes," Hanson said to himself, "The old confrontation."

A panhandler came up to him half a block from the courthouse, "Hey man, you got any spare change?"

"No."

"Quarters, dimes, nickels? Everything helps."

"I said *no*, OK?"

"OK, man. Thanks a lot. Have a nice day."

Another one began drifting towards Hanson. Without breaking stride Hanson hissed, "Get the fuck out of here," and the panhandler drifted away.

Hanson felt good, full of energy. He looked up at the frail, high clouds. "Cirrus," he said to himself. He heard horns honk, and people shouting. He smiled as he turned the corner. It was like going on stage.

Pickets were walking the sidewalk with the usual anti-war signs, cops were standing by, and people in passing cars slowed to curse the demonstrators.

Hanson smiled, did a little dance step, and thought, "hoo-ray-for, *Hollywood.*" Then he noticed a sign he'd never seen before, "There are things I would die for, but nothing I would kill for–CAMUS." It was carried by a man with a full beard and earnest eyes.

226

"Who's that guy, kay-mus?" Hanson asked, "I've never heard of him."

"Cuh-moo. French existentialist."

"A what?"

"It's a kind of philosophy. It's kind of hard to explain. Like, it's a way of dealing with things in the present, without undue concern for the past. The idea that existence precedes essence is. . . ."

A car drove by, honking its horn. A man in a gray workshirt leaned out of the window and yelled, "Fuck you. There's a lot of things I'd kill for. Treason is one of them."

The car made a hard right, the rear tires shrieking and boiling blue smoke.

"Well," Hanson said, "I guess they don't know who that Camus guy is either. You got to consider your audience when you make these things up."

He walked on, and stopped at the two granite and brass monuments, both of them headed, "THEY MADE THE EXTREME SACRIFICE." Columns of raised brass letters, the names of the dead, were ranked below in alphabetical order. He pressed his hand against the names, then looked at his palm. The names, "Forest, Foster, Foster, Fraiser, Fra . . ." were red against the skin, reversed in a mirror image. A limestone soldier atop the WWI monument was running, his rifle in one hand, motioning "follow me" with the other. His face and hands were shriveled and pocked, eaten away by the downtown smog. His features were sloughing off in carbon monoxide instead of mustard gas.

A bearded man with long, honey-colored hair, clutching an American flag around him like a cloak, was being dragged down the steps by several policemen. The cops had little American flags on the shoulders of their uniforms. The man's mouth and beard were bloody, but he kept yelling, "I'm wearing the flag. I'm wearing the flag."

One of the cops muttered, "Get a little stick-time in on this asshole. . . . "

A photographer went along with them in an awkward crouch walk, his camera to his face, twisting the lens as he moved.

The draft board office was packed with demonstrators and policemen, plainclothesmen in suits, and others costumed to mix with the protesters, but obvious by their eyes and by the deliberate way they moved in contrast to the theatrical outrage of the protesters. Their eyes panned across the room, taking in everything.

A craggy-faced man in a gray suit sat on a folding chair in the back of the room. He had a gas mask strapped to his leg, and he looked bored.

Colorful recruiting posters promised travel, adventure, and the chance to become a man. Posters illustrating the points of "The Soldier's Creed" were lined up on the back wall. Point number seven showed a lone soldier hiding behind a log, while enemy soldiers searched the hillside below him. The heading was, "I will never surrender of my own free will." Hanson wondered for a moment how else a person could surrender, that "surrender" implied free will.

"Why are we involved in the internal affairs of the Republic of Vietnam?"

"Why are Americans dying to keep a dictator in office?"

A single secretary sitting behind a low counter was the only available target for the demonstrators' questions. She pressed her lips together and worked at typing out a blue form.

A TV crew moved their lights and cameras to the front of the room, and the rhetoric grew more passionate once the

228

speakers knew that they were being filmed, that they would be watching themselves on the five o'clock news.

"How can you," one of them demanded, pointing at the secretary, "participate in a system that results in the murder and maiming of innocent men, women, and children?"

The secretary ignored him.

"I will not be ignored."

"Right on."

"Tell it."

"I asked you a question, Miss."

The secretary looked up, and said, "I'm not at liberty to discuss it."

"Aren't government employees allowed to think?"

"Right on."

"I vas only following der orders."

Hanson didn't like the tight-lipped secretary, and he didn't like the people who were bullying her. He walked down the hall to the elevator and rode it to the fifth floor.

The E-7 was working a crossword puzzle in the morning paper. He often said that the crossword puzzle was the only thing worth reading in the paper. He was stuck on 3-across, "never gets wet." He turned to the E-5 at the other desk.

"These damn things use 'never' and 'always' too much. You know? There's always exceptions."

The E-5 was looking out the window, the muscles in his jaws working, watching the demonstrators below. He nodded his head, and said "Uh-huh."

Both men wore patches on their shoulders that reproduced, in four colors, the cracked liberty bell, the insignia of the U.S. Army recruiting branch.

The E-7 looked up. A young man with shoulder-length hair was standing in the doorway.

The E-7 thought, *Oh, shit. I thought they were gonna stay down at the draft-board.*

The young man waved his hand grandly and said, "Hiya Sarge, I've come to enlist."

He seemed to be alone. The hall behind him was empty. No hand-lettered signs, no other hippies, none of those pretty girls with long hair. For a moment, the E-7 was disappointed. While most of them did just chant things like, "Pigs-pigs, killers-killers," and those rhymes like "One-two-three-four, we don' want your fucking war," there were usually a couple of those pretty girls who would talk to him, try to *persuade* him to see their side of things. They were friendly, coaxing him along because they thought that he was of course too stupid to see their side all by himself. It beat crossword puzzles.

"Well," the E-7 said, "You've come to the right place. Pull up a chair. Will Gorden," he said, and extended his hand.

"John Hanson."

The E-7 nodded toward the E-5, "Sgt. Cook."

"How you doin', Sgt. Cook," Hanson said.

"Just. Fine. Thanks."

The E-7 glared at Sgt. Cook, and he looked back out the window.

"Well then," the E-7 said, "here's some forms you'll have to fill out. Just take them into that other room over there, there's a desk and some pens. If you have any questions, just holler out."

He escorted Hanson to the room and closed the frosted glass door. When he walked back into the main room, Sgt. Cook had the phone in his hand.

"Yeah, already got 'em on the line."

The E-7 went back to his crossword puzzle.

Sgt. Cook held the phone to his ear, "Uh-huh. Uh-huh. You sure? That's Hanson. S.O.N. OK. Thanks a lot, Jack. Yeah, I know. Be talkin' to you."

The E-7 swiveled his chair around.

"No police record," Sgt. Cook said. "Clean as a whistle. I had Jack double-check. Not even a drug bust."

Hanson came back in, and handed the forms to the E-7.

"I think I filled in all the right little boxes, Sarge. Lotta little boxes to join the army."

The E-7 leafed through them. Outside they could hear a garbled voice on a bullhorn.

"Three years of college, huh?"

"Yep."

"Good. Good, that's real fine. Why don't you come on back here after lunch? That'll give me time to look through these, and all you'll have to do is sign on the line."

He ruffled the papers, then said, "If you don't mind my asking, what made you decide to enlist?"

"Well, Sarge, it took me a couple of days to work it out, but I decided that the simplest thing would be to join up and be a Green Beret. 'Fighting soldiers from the sky,' and all that."

"That's a fine outfit."

The E-7 stood, they shook hands again, and Hanson started to leave, when the E-7 said, "Say, John, would you take a look at this for me? It's the only one I haven't gotten yet."

Hanson looked at the folded newspaper, "never gets wet," he read aloud. He studied it for a moment, then picked up a pencil and filled in the missing letters.

"I think that's what they want, Sarge. It's the 'right answer,' but–it's not really right, you know? *I* could think of a way to get it wet. It's just too absolute a statement to say that it never gets wet. What about a broken dam, or a tidal wave, or a tornado?

"See you after lunch then," Hanson said, smiling. He gave the two men a snappy little salute and walked out.

"I'd like to be that cocky little bastard's drill sergeant," Sgt. Cook said. "Basic Training is gonna be surprise city for him. Gonna be hurt city. Green Beret, shit. He'll be the US Army's first astronaut before he gets through Special Forces."

"You just haven't been here long enough to *appreciate* things, young Sergeant. I been feeling like some kind of used car salesman lately. All we been getting through here is slack-jaw niggers, high school drop-outs, and people who had a choice of the army or jail. Shit. Three years of college, and *no* record."

He waved the sheaf of forms, "I'm gonna make sure the Captain sees this. This is gonna buy me a three-day weekend."

"Never get through basic."

Hanson strutted out the entrance to the courthouse, grinning. He'd faked those dumb-ass recruiters out of their olive-drab shorts. "I want to be a Greeeeen Beret." They didn't know whether to shit or go blind.

"'Well, that's a fine outfit, son.' That's right, Sarge, you slave merchant. We'll see."

Hanson had things pretty well figured out. All it would take would be a little determination, and getting through the Army would be a cinch.

He stopped and glanced at the cadaverous doughboy on top of the WWI monument. It occurred to him that "Doughboy" was the name of the cute little man that advertised dinner rolls on TV.

A car slowed down and someone demanded to know why he didn't move to Russia.

2

It was late afternoon when Hanson noticed the orange poster tacked to a phone pole he was passing. Beneath a blurred photo of a crowd holding placards and banners were the words, "INTERESTED IN WORKING FOR REAL CHANGE? FOR TRUE CONTROL OF YOUR LIFE? FOR AUTHENTIC FREEDOM?"

He smiled and thought, "Some of that authentic freedom." His thirty-day leave before going back to Vietnam was almost over and he was glad, tired of waiting.

A pretty young woman in a long peasant dress crossed the street to him and handed him one of the posters. "Hi," she said, "do you know about the rally and the non-competitive games over at Sears Park tomorrow?" looking into his eyes as if she'd been looking for him all her life.

"What are non-competitive games?" he asked.

"Games," she said, "where you cooperate rather than compete, where there are no winners or losers."

"But how do you have a game without competition? How do the rules work?"

"Rules aren't important," she said, smiling into his eyes.

"I don't understand," Hanson said.

"You will," she said, "we have Frisbee tossing, and a game called the people-pass. We stand close together and lift one

233

person up, over our heads, and pass him along. The person being lifted has to trust the people holding him up. It's a lesson in cooperation, about the danger of resisting and not trusting."

"I see," Hanson said, folding the poster and tucking it into his hip pocket, "I'll come by if I can, thanks."

"Be happy," she said, her face radiant.

A foot bridge led into the park. Sears Park had once been green and pleasant, but in the past few years people who were "just passing through" had been using it as a campground and the grass was dying, littered with empty cans, plastic bags, and empty bottles of Honeyrose Tokay wine.

The park was crowded, and dust rose from patches of dirt where the grass had been worn away. Hanson passed an emaciated speed freak who looked up from where he was lying in the dirt and asked him, "Spare change?" Hanson kept walking and the voice followed him, "Man, you don't care, man. But you should, you should, man. You don't know me, you don't know me, man. . . . "

The smell of dogshit hung over the park, and snot-nosed children with names like "Harmony" and "Sunshine" dug in the dirt with sticks. Someone was playing a guitar badly. He passed a kid sitting on a rope-bound bedroll next to a big, sick-looking dog, the kid staring at his hands and wiggling his fingers.

Barefoot, shirtless young men were throwing Frisbees, spinning to catch them behind their backs, or between their legs, throwing them to their dogs, then having to chase the dogs and pry the scarred Frisbee loose while the dog growled and resisted.

The sun was down as he jumped the fence to cross the golf course. It was a weekday and there were only two groups of golfers in sight. They rode in white golf carts, lurching along like slapstick Staff Officers toward the clubhouse. Hanson could hear their clubs rattling like something shaking a cage.

He crossed the golf course, entering an older residential section of town. As he walked past one house he saw the blue light of a television and could hear the tinny sound of gunshots, a western or a special on the war, he supposed. The sky was clearer than usual, less polluted, and Hanson saw, or thought he saw, a silver satellite coursing easily through the other stars, indifferent and effortless. He lost sight of it as the street lights clicked on and buzzed overhead. A rabbit froze on a lawn, its flat head pointed in the direction Hanson was walking, watching him through the limpid black eye on the side of its head.

The Pick-Wick was a small, narrow bar with a stamped-tin ceiling. It was sandwiched in between a drugstore and a Bi-Rite Market. There were booths along one wall, and a bar on the other, leaving just enough room for two people to squeeze past each other. The clientele was mostly regulars, students, teachers, musicians, newspaper people, and a few railroad workers who had been drinking there for twenty years. Newspaper clippings, photos, and posters, most of them yellowed and curling, were taped or tacked to the walls. A garishly tinted stuffed swordfish hung over the bar mirror. The mirror was a patchwork of bounced checks, photos of Ted Williams and, for racial balance, Willy Mays, Betty Grable, Dizzy Gillespie playing, his neck and cheeks puffed out, and photos of all the past Pick-Wick softball teams. Old license plates covered one wall, and the place was full of the good smell of beer, hamburgers, and onions.

The Pick-Wick looked the same. It seemed slightly dimmer, though. Darker than Hanson had remembered it. "Memory," Hanson thought, "or just a burned-out neon light." Still, it seemed like the bar had aged since he'd been there last, like a person ages, losing a little energy every year, half-lives, the whole universe running down. Everything dies, he thought. Most people don't really know that. He had not known it the last time he was here. The vaguely familiar faces had aged slightly, not quickly like the face of someone dying on the ground in front of you, but it was the same, only gradual. There were new faces, younger faces, too.

There was a new bartender, someone Hanson didn't know.

Freddie Johnson was sitting on a stool near the door.

Freddie had gotten a medical discharge from the Navy six weeks after enlisting. He'd spent days in the library before he'd joined, studying psychology texts and medical journals, composing his own set of symptoms, and it had worked. He'd gotten a medical discharge for having claustrophobia so severe that he couldn't function in the steel confines of a ship.

"Hey, Freddie, how you doin'?" Hanson said as he walked past. "How's the claustrophobia?"

"Only bothers me when I get near a ship. I heard you were back. How you doin'?"

"Doin' good."

Tommy Curtiss was at the bar, near the back. He looked smaller than Hanson had remembered him, cherubic face, shock of curly red hair. Tommy was a trumpet player. There had been a time when Hanson would stay with his wife every time Tommy was out of town on a "gig."

"Hanson, how you doin' man. Long time."

"Good, Tommy, how you been?"

Tommy lifted his beer, smiled, and nodded his head.

"Good," Hanson said.

Tommy drained his beer, and said, "Gotta split, man, catch you later." He swiveled off the barstool and walked out.

Hanson sat down at the bar.

The dollar bill was still taped to the mirror behind the bar, the tape holding it there was brown and curling. The bill had been written on with a felt-tip pen, "For Hanson's first beer when he gets back home." Marvin had written the words and taped the bill to the mirror the night before Hanson had left for the West Coast and on to Vietnam. Marvin had told him it was "insurance." But that same night, when Hanson had said his good-byes and started out the door, Marvin had called out, "Hey, Bud. Don't go."

Hanson had turned, shrugged, smiled and said, "Aw Marvin. Shit. You take care. See you next year."

Marvin owned the Pick-Wick. He was a stocky man, in his early 50s. He tended bar a couple nights a week, but he made most of his money handling the numbers and punch-board concessions throughout the county, for which he paid off the local sheriff. It was also said that he did a lot of serious card-playing at the Elks club on Tuesdays and Thursdays.

Marvin never raised his voice except sometimes when he laughed.

One night several bikers from out of town had come in, and began to casually bully some of the other customers. Marvin walked to their table and said, "I'm sorry, but I'm going to have to ask you gentlemen to leave."

They looked up at him. One of them nodded and they all got up and left.

Hanson's eyes adjusted to the dim light and cigarette smoke, and he saw Charlie at the end of the bar. Charlie, a head taller than anyone else in the place, built like a fullback, shoulder-length blond hair, and flashing rimless glasses. He was waving his hands around like an evangelist, telling a story.

" . . . then this *crazy* guy comes walking up. He's wearing three coats, two pairs of pants, a yellow cab driver's cap. . . ."

Charlie liked to refer to himself as "the old outlaw." He refused to let anyone take his picture, and had once smashed a TV camera when he accidentally walked into a "man-on-the-street" interview. "Do I look like the kind of person who'd talk to a woman wearing a microphone? I mean, get this shit out of my face."

He moved every few months, skipping out on his rent payments and utility bills, but he always paid his phone bill. He talked to people all over the country, but he had attached an electronic device to the phone so that his calls were never recorded. He always paid his small monthly phone bills for local service, saying, "Those fuckers at the phone company will track you down if you owe 'em money. They know who your friends are, your family, they know everything. I don't fuck with the phone company."

He had a floating post office box, and he belonged to every "of the month" club there was, book of the month, record of the month, plant, fruit, ham of the month, tape of the month, California wine of the month. Whenever he found an ad with a box on it that said, "Bill me," he sent for whatever it offered.

When Hanson was home on leave after basic training he'd run into Charlie who told him, "Let's take a ride. Some *fool* sent me an Esso Credit card." They drove fifty miles up the interstate and fifty miles back, stopping at every Esso station, using the credit card and stuffing the trunk of Charlie's GTO with oil, spark plugs, tune-up kits, Turtle wax, and eating Stewart's Raydar-Range Hot sandwiches at the stations. They kept the total under $50.00 at each station so the attendant wouldn't call the credit card hotline and find out that Charlie owed over three thousand dollars on the card.

Twenty miles from home, they spotted a police roadblock. Charlie hit the brakes, skidded the car ninety degrees, and headed cross-country. As they bounced and plowed across a soybean field, Hanson said, "It's just a routine check."

"Tell me about it. Take a look in the glove box."

The glove box was stuffed with pink, green, and yellow traffic citations, wadded in so tight that they'd sprung the hinge.

"If those cops run my name," Charlie had said, the GTO hopping furrows, dragging a tangle of soybean vines, "if they run my *initials,* there's a big neon sign down at headquarters that's gonna light up and flash 'JACKPOTJACKPOTJACK-POT!'"

Hanson laughed, remembering it. Charlie was so big he could wear his hair as long as he wanted, whatever clothes he wanted—once he'd shown up in a war bonnet, another time in tails and a top hat—and no one bothered him. And he was one of the few people Hanson knew who approved of his being in the Army.

"Great," he'd said, "think of all those great weapons they'll give you, machine-guns, bazookas, grenades. Fifty-caliber stuff. Hell, one of those will kill somebody three miles away. I'd join up myself, but I got too many deals going right now. Just be careful. It's not worth getting killed over."

"Hey, Charles," Hanson called, "where haff you bin, boy? What you been up to?"

"Hanson, my man," Charlie shouted, "I heard you were back. Another beer here, darlin'," he said to the bar maid. He motioned Hanson to a booth, and set two beers down.

"Well, I have been pretty mobile lately, if you get my drift. I heard that some folks were looking for me, and I didn't really want to talk to them.

"Hey," he said, "do *you* know anybody who might be interested in buying a sewing machine? At a good price? Dial-a-stitch, zigzag, automatic button holes?"

Hanson shook his head.

"No? I didn't think so. Damn. I saw this ad about becoming a sewing machine salesman. 'Be your own boss.' You know the type. 'Limited only by your own imagination and initiative. Pick your own hours.' That kind of stuff. Picture of this seedy guy showing a machine to a woman in a night gown, she's smiling at him and got her leg cocked up. Like there's all these housewives out there who want to buy a sewing machine *and* get laid.

"Anyway, if you sign up, they send you a demonstrator. Haw. That got my attention. I got the sucker out in the truck, but nobody needs a sewing machine. I was gonna give it to Maureen–remember her?–but she got pissed off at me for something and moved to California. Good place for her."

"The truck?" Hanson asked him, "Where's the GTO?"

"I had to give it a little rest. Too many people looking for a red GTO."

"Your truck that old Dodge out front?"

"That's her. Power Wagon. Slept in it last night. Been here since they opened up this morning."

The bar suddenly got quiet.

At the far wall, over the potato chip rack, a grease and smoke stained TV hung on a plywood swing. Lyndon Johnson was staring from the screen, gazing over the booths, through the front window, out into the dark. His voice was ragged as he announced another troop increase in Vietnam.

The barmaid rolled up a wet dishtowel, snapped it at the TV, and hit the on/off/volume button. "That's enough of that shit," she said.

The president's face vanished. There were cheers and applause, and the bar returned to normal. Except for Charlie. He was muttering to himself, and Hanson realized that he was drunker than he had seemed to be.

"That fucker," Charlie said. " *'Mah fellow Amarucuns.'* You know, there are millions of TVs in this country. *Hundreds* of millions, and that evil redneck is stomping, and preaching, and staring out of every one of 'em like some Holy Baptist Yazoo. He's got his evil little eyes on all of us."

Charlie was waving his hands around like a signalman, "He can't just say, 'I'm gonna do this, I'm gonna do that.' Him and his buddies. All the fat cats. He's not the fuckin' King, you know. He's not *royalty.*"

"Come on," he said, getting to his feet, "I been thinking about it, and I know what we gotta do."

He staggered into a barstool, then made his way outside. Hanson followed.

Charlie was walking in little circles in front of the Pick-Wick, muttering. "Yeah," he said, "yeah. Out there. Golf courses. They're out there riding on those little carts and hitting those stupid little balls while the shit is coming down. They're all making money on the war. You know what?" he said, walking over to Hanson. "I think," he said, lowering his voice, "that golf is a symbol of everything that's wrong with this country."

He walked back into the Pick-Wick and came back out with a beer that he drained in four swallows. He took a two-gallon gas can out of the back of the truck and used it to fill the empty beer bottle, knocking the bottle over once, and getting most of the gas on the sidewalk. He held the bottle by the neck, at eye level, then he looked at the truck, at the Pick-Wick, down the street, then laughed and set the bottle down.

He ripped a piece of his shirt-tail off, stuffed it into the neck of the bottle, and said, "Let's go to the golf course.

"Watch out for the sewing machine."

Hanson noticed that the truck had a new Hurst floorshift, so he wasn't surprised when Charlie started the engine and the torque rocked the old truck like a rowboat. He looked at Charlie.

"Yeah," he said, "I tuned her up a little. Got all the high-performance stuff with my American Express card. I got a box of Louisiana mangos in here somewhere. Look out for 'em, they must be pretty ripe by now. Probably crawling with goddamn tarantulas. I should have left 'em at the P.O. Or thrown 'em away. Thought I could sell 'em."

The truck burned rubber in the first two gears.

"Who'd I think was gonna buy mangos around here?"

He burned rubber in fourth gear, and the speedometer hit fifty. Hanson looked back, and he could still see the lights of the Pick-Wick.

Charlie was steering with both hands, holding the bottle of gasoline between his legs. "I got a couple duffel bags of dope in the back. Great stuff. Having some problems unloading it, though."

Near the golf course now, half the houses they passed were imitation Southern plantations with pillars, circular drives, and cast-iron artificial niggers, dressed like jockeys, whipping invisible horses. Their headlights swept past one iron jockey whose face and hands had been painted pink.

"Goddamn neighborhood liberal," Charlie yelled, "I hate a liberal. Rather have George Wallace in the White House than some half-ass knee-jerk liberal."

He pulled the truck over the curb near the seventh hole, jumped out, and stormed the manicured grass knoll, Molotov cocktail in hand, grunting, "Blow this fucker up," and something about a "firestorm."

Hanson was afraid he'd set himself on fire, and tried to convince him that the best thing would be to lay the bottle down next to the rod that held the little flag.

"Naw," he said, "that won't work. This is a Molotov cocktail. You gotta throw these things to blow anything up. Look out!"

He lit the cloth and threw the bottle bouncing toward the seventh hole. It rolled to a stop and what gasoline was left burned for half a minute, scorching a little divot out of the green.

"Hell's bells," Charlie roared, "that sure didn't work like in the movies." He began laughing, and put his arm around Hanson. "Life's full of disappointments isn't it?" he said, "Let's go get another beer."

3

Washington D.C.–Ft. Holabird

Hanson was wearing worn Levi's, a blue cotton work shirt, and an old pair of tennis shoes. He had on a brass belt buckle that was the shape of a shooting star. His shirtsleeves were rolled up to the elbow, a deep tan covering the freckles on his forearms. A red spot on the inside of his elbow began to sting, and he looked at it. A tiny piece of copper wire, the color of his hair, that had blown back from the ignition assembly of an anti-tank rocket, was slowly working its way out of the skin.

He looked out the plastic porthole, glancing up at the light cloud cover, then watched a cheerful young man, about his own age, walking alongside the airliner, guiding it out onto the runway. He was wearing fat red ear protectors over a red baseball cap, and he began a kind of ritual dance. Turning toward the front of the plane, he spread his arms, palms down, as though he were smoothing something out. He turned toward the rear of the plane and repeated the movement. Then he put his arms up, palms toward each other as though he were showing the length of a fish he might have caught, and the plane's engines began to rev, pulling at the brakes. The young man watched, and seemed to be listening through the ear protectors. He pointed his left arm toward the runway. Then he smiled, saluted the cockpit, turned on his heel and walked away, moving easily through the traffic of forklifts, baggage tractors, and self-propelled conveyer belts.

The plane taxied toward the twin row of strobe lights that flashed in sequence, flickering like lightning down the runway. The stewardess began her pantomime, pointing vaguely toward emergency exits, and a Muzak version of "Mr. Tambourine Man" faded into the rising whine of the jet engines.

He looked for her in the crowd, and then discovered that she was standing almost next to him. He smelled her perfume before he saw her. She looked different, unfamiliar, something about her eyes. It had been over a year since he had seen her. She had long black hair, wideset eyes, and high cheekbones that almost suggested Indian blood. When he kissed her he tasted cigarette smoke. The tight acetate dress that she was wearing came well above her knees, and the material was slick beneath his hand.

"Hi," she said, "so how are you?" a hint of a Boston accent in her voice. "That haircut is amazing. You really are in the Army then?"

"So it seems," Hanson said, pulling a black baseball cap out of his back pocket and putting it on. "I shaved it in jump school once. Too many lumps and scars though, it looked like I'd had multiple lobotomies. I guess the lobotomy look was inappropriate. I shaved it because they screamed at me, every day, that my hair was too long. After I shaved my head they told me that, if the top of my head got sunburned so I couldn't, uh, participate, they could court martial me for destruction of government property."

They watched the parade of luggage groaning and thumping past them on the conveyer belt.

"So how long will you be here?"

"Two months. I'll be taking the Special Forces Operations and Intelligence course. Classified Spook stuff, it should be fun. Then I'm off to the war."

His fat green duffel bag rumbled through the rubber-flap door on the conveyer belt, lumpy and out of place among the sleek Samsonites and American Touristers. He worked his way through the knot of impatient businessmen holding their briefcases and carry-on bags, snatched the duffel bag up with one hand, and used it like a shield to clear a patch back to where she was.

He was boyish in his baseball cap and jeans, but his eyes were all wrong. They focused like cameras stopping down at a pair of salesmen who stepped in front of him, then widened just as quickly when he smiled at her, as if a switch had gone from "on" to "off." As they walked down the concourse, he kept track of the people around them by watching their reflections sliding across the shop windows.

Outside, it was hot and humid. He could taste the smog. Beyond the thickets of chainlink fence a jet took off, laying a carpet of black smoke.

"Are you OK?" she said. "You seem kind of nervous or angry about something."

"Yeah, it's all these people. I'm not used to being in crowds like this. Nobody watches where they're going, so I have to watch for them. It pisses me off."

"Hey," he said, putting his arm, a little awkwardly, around her shoulders, "I'm glad to see you. I'm glad you're here." Her hair smelled of cigarette smoke and perfume, and was damp with perspiration at the base of her neck. "I'll be OK once we get away from this place."

He threw his duffel bag into the back of her yellow Karman Ghia convertible and slouched down in the bucket seat, pulling the black cap over his eyes against the afternoon sun. As she worked the car through the busy parking lot, he tried to relax, tried not to pay attention to the other cars and potential collisions.

The parking lot attendant had his hair pulled back into a pony tail with rubber bands. His back was to them, showing a peace symbol painted like a bull's-eye on the army fatigue shirt he was wearing.

They pulled up to the attendant's booth, she put the car in neutral, and they waited. The attendant was looking away from them, listening to a radio that was turned up loud enough to cover the sound of their engine.

Hanson sat in the car, staring straight ahead, hearing the same three bass chords, over and over like a taunt coming from the radio. A dark blue Buick pulled up behind them, looming over the little yellow sports car, trapping it against the red and white striped barrier.

The driver behind them tapped his horn. Hanson looked back at the Buick, over at Betty, and up at the peace symbol on the attendant's back. The Buick honked again.

Hanson vaulted out of the car and marched back to the Buick. He slapped the windshield with his open hand and kicked the door. "OK," he yelled, "all right. That's enough fucking noise," he shouted at the reflected glare from the windshield. He slapped the glass again, and the Buick backed quickly away, lurching from side to side.

Hanson turned, walked to the attendant's shack, and kicked the door open. As he switched the radio off the attendant spun around. "What the fuck's your problem, man?" he said. He had a pointed blond beard and a small red mouth.

With the radio off, small sounds seemed suddenly loud– the hum of a power line overhead, the faraway sound of traffic, the creak of the floor as the attendant shifted his weight. Hanson could feel his own face flush, feel the tiny pulse over his eye. He pulled a dollar bill out of his pocket and slammed it down on a plywood table. "Here," he said, "open the gate."

"You're not authorized in here, man," the attendant said.

"There's the buck for the parking fee," Hanson said, then hit him with the heel of his hand high on the chest, snapping his head back. "Open the little gate before I break it off and shove it up your ass. And don't call me *man,*" he said, and straight-armed him again in the chest, *"man."*

"OK. OK. No problem."

Hanson got back into the car, the barrier swung up, and they drove out of the parking lot.

Betty looked at him, then back at the road. "What have they been teaching you?" she said. "You used to be a, uh," she laughed, "kind of a nice guy."

"That phony dork with the peace-sign fatigue shirt. Tells me I'm not 'authorized.' The *nice* guys I've seen this last year didn't make it. They end up crying and bleeding on the floor while everybody laughs at them. What they've been teaching me is that if you let someone start fucking with you, they're not going to stop until you make them, so you might as well stop it right away. In the Army they take everything from you. *Everything.* Including the person you were, or thought you were before they got you."

He slapped himself on the chest. "This," he said, then tapped his forehead with his finger, "and this. That's all I've got."

They rode in silence for a minute, then Hanson laughed and said, "And don't call me *man,* man.

"He thinks he's gonna give *me* some shit? I could have *killed* the guy. He tells me I'm not *authorized?*"

"Jesus," she said, "are you all right? You haven't gotten real weird or anything, have you?"

"Not me," he said, "not me." He leaned over and whispered in her ear, hard and mean, "Just don't call me *man,* man," then he began to laugh. "I'll tell you all about it, but it'll take a while."

He watched her legs as she shifted gears. They were dancer's legs, and the sun caught the downy gold hair below the hem of her dress.

They drove into the sun, past an old cemetery where the rows of stones threw long shadows. The patterns of simple stones were dominated by monuments topped with thick-winged angels. A pair of figures, their outlines lost in the sun, walked among the graves.

The little car rumbled downhill over cobblestones, past brown row-houses where old women sat on their stoops and watched them pass. Cardboard placards on sticks, driven into the tiny dead lawns, announced the names of political candidates. At the outer edge of the city the black spires and smoked-stone foundations of the riot-burned empty blocks looked like solid shadows.

They stopped for traffic on a block lined with bars and burlesque marquees where fat, sweating men in shirtsleeves stood outside, taunting passersby, insulting them, somehow, into the strip shows.

"Hey friend, don't walk off now. These girls will make you feel young again."

"Hey-hey-hey, it's showtime inside. Right now. It's show-time. The pretty girls are all inside and it's showtime. . . . "

"A wise choice not to go in there," another hawker interrupted as a man passed by, "that place is a hot-dog stand. Now *we* have got. . . . "

Prostitutes, in pairs and groups of three, walked the street talking and laughing among themselves, joking with the hawkers, primping in the mirrors of liquor store windows. They were exotic and bluntly sensuous, raw and funky.

Hanson smiled at a pretty black woman in hot pink shorts and matching halter. She pouted at him and wiggled her hips. Hanson grinned, embarrassed. The woman laughed and cupped her breasts in her hands, offering them to him.

A wino lurched out at the car, a crusty rag in his hand. He stumbled into the car shouting, "Clean your windshield." His eyes were red and watery, and he had a fresh cut on his forehead. For an instant Hanson thought he had been hit by traffic and thrown into their car. He could smell the stink of his breath on the hot afternoon air. Betty drove on while the wino stood swaying in the middle of the street, screaming at them.

"Welcome to Washington," Betty said.

She pulled off into a noisy deadend street where soul music and Puerto Rican dance music poured out of open windows, parking in front of an abandoned-looking storefront. Fading red letters on the front window said, "ELECTRO LOCK & ALARM–Installed+Opened+Repaired–Deadbolts+Window locks+Door Closers+Panic Bars."

A wino was asleep in the doorway.

"They have to sleep out in the open," she said. "It's too bad. Especially in the winter. They're afraid to sleep in the alleys. The kids set them on fire for fun."

"What's a panic bar?" he asked her, laughing.

"No idea."

"I'd like to have one, whatever it is. Take it with me wherever I go."

She stepped over the wino and opened the police lock on the steel-clad door. "We're home," she said, smiling over her shoulder at Hanson.

The first floor was cluttered with crates, stacks of old newspapers, shopping carts, boxes of plastic cups, party hats, and a dozen bald and broken mannequins staring vacantly across the room. They looked like chemotherapy cancer patients who had lost their hair.

"We don't rent the downstairs," Betty said, leading him through the clutter to a narrow stairway.

"I don't think anybody's home," she said. "Larry and Marsha got a movie gig. I don't know where Ron is."

The door opened into a narrow hallway. Sections of plaster had scabbed off, showing the lath below, like dried ribs. They passed a little telephone nook in the wall that had been turned into a sort of shrine, occupied by a painted and gilt plaster Christ holding his own bloody heart in his hands. His eyes had been painted out, a hollow socket black. Stale incense almost covered the odor of old food and the sharp stink of cat piss, the smell of old newspapers, old plaster, mildew, and marijuana.

"Movie gig?" Hanson asked her.

"Porn movies. Your basic dirty movie. They get fifty dollars a day when they're working."

"How did you meet these interesting people?"

"I used to know Ron at school. He introduced me to Larry and Marsha, and we all found this place together."

"And what does your man Ron do?"

"Whatever will get him by. He's dealing some sunshine acid right now. It's really fine acid. We'll have to do some."

"Really fine, huh? And what have you and Ron got going?"

"Nothing. We did for a while, but not any more. We're friends," she said.

Hanson looked at her.

"Are you going to turn prudish on me or what?" she said, "It was no world-class affair."

"You tell that motherfucker to stay out of my way. Out of my sight, OK? I don't want to even see him. I got enough loony tunes in the Army. I don't need this weird shit."

"Hey," she said softly, "don't. It's going to be nice. Whatever you say, that's fine. Please? Let's take your stuff up to my room. It's nice up there. We're all by ourselves. It's the only room on that floor, nobody else comes up there. Come on," she said, taking his hand.

On the next landing they walked through a large room that was completely decorated with turn-of-the-century furniture, lamps and drapes. It was gloomy, musty from all the faded and stained overstuffed velvet chairs and black velvet curtains. Dust particles boiled in a single ray of sunlight coming through a gap in the curtains. A porcelain statuette of a dancer held up a fringed lampshade with the stumps of her missing hands. Stained leather-bound books and yellowing magazines were stacked on a coffee table that stood on stuffed deer legs and hooves. A cast iron crucifix the size of a lug wrench stood on a low table in front of the fireplace, flanked by fat black candles.

A gray cat slipped through the door behind them, watched them for a moment, then vanished.

"Interesting room," Hanson said.

"But it really is. Larry decorated it. He's into a lot of things —macrobiotics, reincarnation—he just does the movies because it's easy bread. He likes to sit in here, he says, and feel the presence of the people who used to own all this stuff, and the people who used to live here."

They took another narrow flight of stairs to her room, squeaking, winding, narrow stairs that led to a small garret room that was fresh and clean, with a carpet and a canopy bed. There were two windows, one with a view of the street, the other of a garbage-littered courtyard. A pleasant room, but he couldn't shake off the feeling he'd gotten down in the lower room. As he looked out the window to the courtyard, the gray cat, defecating on the concrete below, grinned up at him.

Betty put her arms around him. "Come on," she said, "relax now. It's just you and me here."

"Yeah. Look, you tell those people who live here that I don't want them in this room, ever. I don't want them up here. Tell 'em that the Army made me crazy, that I'll kill anybody who comes up here."

"Sure. I'll tell them." She pressed herself against him and smiled up at him. "We've got clean sheets and some wine."

Hanson glanced over her shoulder and saw a painting of a woman's face on the wall. It reminded him of her, but the features were strangely distorted.

"Is that a self-portrait?" he asked her.

"That painting? Yeah, that's me. I painted it by looking into a mirror when I was tripping."

Late that night, half asleep, Hanson heard voices and music on the floor below, flutes and bells. The low voices were monotonous and rhythmical. He shifted himself into the soft hollow of Betty's body, into a deeper sleep, and dreamed about the field survival exercise at the Special Forces School, the first one, the one where they'd killed small animals with their hands and used knives on the goats.

It was on the fourth or fifth day, February in the woods, where there had been a steady cold rain since the night they parachuted in. They'd had no food at all and less than three hours sleep each night in the mud, forced marches through the swamps, planning ambushes at night with red-lensed flashlights hidden beneath the dripping shelter halves. It was the week they used to wash out Special Forces recruits who couldn't or wouldn't suck up the pain and keep going. The week that won them the right to wear the beret.

The chickens were simple. You just pulled their heads off, then held them quickly away from you, like a champagne bottle you've just uncorked, while the neck pumped blood.

The rabbit they gave him was big, the size of a small dog, white with glittering pink eyes. He held it by its hind legs, its head toward the ground. It struggled in his hand at first, then arched its back, suddenly rigid, its head back, clearly exposing the muscled vee where the neck fit into the shoulders. He held it up with his left hand and chopped down hard, with the edge of his hand, into the vee. The head, with its thick, delicately pink-veined ears, popped off, spinning to the ground, while the heavy warm body shuddered and leaped in his hand, like a bird trying to take flight.

But it was the goat that he remembered most clearly. It was tied between two trees, bawling and lunging against the ropes as tirelessly as a machine. A lot of animals had been killed that day, the blood smell was riding the light rain, and the goat was wild with panic. He kept braying and running out the little slack the ropes gave him, hitting the end of the slack, the ropes throwing him back.

Hanson tried to look into his eyes as he walked toward the goat, but the animal refused to make eye contact, looking away, refusing to acknowledge what he knew was about to happen to him.

Hanson went around behind the goat, straddled it, and twisted one of its ears to keep it from bucking. The animal

253

was warm and wet between his legs as he dug his heels into the mud to keep control, the wet wool stinking of musk, mud, shit and wood smoke. The goat arched its neck, and for an instant Hanson saw, reflected in the animal's wild, dark eye, the pine trees, the watching soldiers, and his own distorted face.

An icy rain fell steadily, hissing through the trees, turning the ground and sky a grayish green. Hanson pulled up and back on the goat's jaw with his left hand, and drove the heavy blade of the K-bar knife into him, through the muscle between spine and windpipe, then pulled the knife down and through the windpipe and out the front of the neck.

The goat stopped braying because the vocal cords had been cut away from the air supply. He began to blow steam and gouts of blood through the severed windpipe—a fine red mist —his breathing loud, wet, and ragged. Then its legs buckled and it dropped beneath Hanson, twitching and kicking, one of its hooves bruising Hanson's shin, and it died.

"All right," the instructor said, "good job. You 'bout took that mother's head off."

One day, years later, it would occur to him that there were no goats or rabbits in Vietnam, that they had not been training him to butcher livestock.

The orange tablet was the size of a printed capital "O," and looked like it had been punched out with a tiny cookie cutter. It had an impression of a peace sign on the top.

Hanson had taken LSD a couple of times, but that had been before he went into the Army, and he had changed since then. He knew that he had changed, and he was a little worried as he put the tablet in his mouth. It was sweet as it melted on his tongue, with a delicate yet powerful orange flavor. It warmed his tongue and jaw as if it were glowing in there. Sunshine acid.

"I feel really good about this," Betty said, "we can really talk behind this, you know? Let's go down to the park and wait for the rush."

It was almost dark, a warm humid evening. They passed a liquor store with glowing neon beer signs and a huge inflated replica of a vodka bottle in the window. A kid rode by them on a bicycle, a playing card clattering against the wheel spokes. Four airliners were visible against the eastern sky, then five of them, stacked up and waiting to land, holding their positions, their landing lights seeming to float like UFOs or evening stars. A bag lady was going through a dumpster in an alley. A black kid walked past, holding a radio to his ear, its thin music moving with him, and a gas main hissed from behind a stack of empty crates. The headlights of passing cars were brilliant, like the light that must dance down in the core of a nuclear reactor.

Hanson realized that he was grinning but he could not make himself stop. Everyone seemed to be looking at him, but he knew it was mostly the paranoia that comes from the drug, and he fought it, knowing that if he let it take him over it could lead to bad violence, to hospitals and jails.

They passed a Greek restaurant that advertised a belly dancer, the photograph of her in a chain-link bra tremendously funny. The windows of the pornography shop next to it were painted out in chalky yellow paint, but through the open door Hanson could see a three-tiered glass case filled with ranks of bright pink dildos of varied heights and thicknesses, like marching columns of little bald soldiers. He could hear drums from the park.

Black men wearing knit caps were playing conga and bongo drums. A pair of Dobermans was pacing around the drummers. In the distance there were sirens. A fat black man wearing cutoff blue jeans and a feathered Indian headdress stormed past them, crying and cursing at the night sky. He staggered into a blonde girl wearing the top half of a high school band uniform, and continued on his way. The girl looked at Hanson, smiled beatifically, and said, "It's cool, he's just working things out."

Hanson laughed and started to walk farther into the park, but Betty grabbed his arm. "Let's get out of here," she said, "this is all a little too crazy, too heavy. Too much bad energy here."

She began to walk away, walking faster and faster until she was almost running.

"Hey," Hanson said to her, putting his arm around her shoulders, stopping her, worried about attracting attention that might lead to the police, and questions, and a court-martial, "everything's fine."

"No it's not. Everything isn't fine. Everything's getting freaky. Did you see that guy back there? The one who was watching me? Is he still back there? Let's keep walking."

Back at the storefront she locked the police lock behind them, jamming the steel rod into the lock hole, "I don't feel so good," she said, "I'm cold."

The walk up to the bedroom seemed to take hours, the passage through the living room full of danger, the stink of incense and cat piss so powerful Hanson could taste it on his tongue. Up in her room, he looked down into the courtyard and saw the gray cat watching the window. When he undressed Betty, her skin was glowing, almost transparent in the electric light, the shadow of her blood throbbing beneath the skin. Hanson wondered if blood really was purple inside the body and turned red only when exposed, in cuts and wounds, to the air.

In the bed he looked down at her beneath him. Her pupils were huge. He got dizzy just looking down into them, and when he touched her lips he thought he could feel what she was feeling.

And then her face began to change, every second, like slides flashed on a screen, exaggerated, pure expressions of anger, fear, sadness, giving way one after another. She began to talk as though he wasn't there, as though she was summoning up conversations from the past with different people, the conversations beginning and ending abruptly in mid-sentence.

Hanson was suddenly exhausted. He could see that he wasn't going to be able to talk to her until the drug wore off, and, with his arm around her, he let himself begin to sink into sleep.

Something woke him, and he realized that she wasn't in the bed with him anymore. He opened his eyes, rolled over, and saw her standing on the ledge outside the window, her naked body glowing in the streetlights and the red and blue neon signs of the tavern windows below, blinking on and off.

"Betty," he said softly from the bed, afraid he might startle her, "come on inside. Come on back in."

She didn't seem to hear him and he slipped out of the bed and walked slowly to the window, talking softly to her as he walked, "Betty, it's me. Can you hear me?"

"Come on inside," he said. A lone car drove by below, and a streetwalker turned the corner at the end of the block.

Betty suddenly crouched and turned to look at Hanson, her eyes a mix of fear and anger, changing in an instant to arrogance, "No," she said, "it's cool out here. The air is cool."

"Here," he said, reaching slowly out to her, "take my hand, and come on inside."

"No," she said, sounding almost serene now, "I like the way the light feels on my skin. This is where I'm supposed to be, this is what John Lennon sang about."

Hanson braced himself against the window frame, then grabbed her arm and pulled, jerking her back through the window. She clawed at his eyes and neck, drawing blood, but he managed to pin her to the floor, holding her down with the weight of his body and controlling her arms with his hands, admiring the small bones moving in her shoulders and upper back. She gurgled and made little barking noises in her throat, tried to arch her neck to bite him in the arm, but couldn't reach him.

After a long time she relaxed and seemed to go to sleep. He loosened his grip on her arms, testing, and she didn't move. He got up off her, and she stayed where she was, breathing easily.

He closed and locked the window, then pushed the bed up against the wall in front of the window. She still slept on the floor next to the bed, as Hanson lay back down, secure in the knowledge that she would have to climb over him to get to the window. He listened to her breathing as he slipped back into a state where he was asleep but still aware of what was going on around him.

Some time later he opened his eyes to see her standing over him with a steak knife in her hand, holding it down at her side, watching him.

Before he moved, he planned which arm to use to block the knife if she brought it up, but she didn't move as he jumped up and grabbed her arm.

"Who do you think you are?" she said. "The home town boy who knocked up the Queen," then she laughed, "in the Navy Yard?"

"Why don't I take that," he said, prying her fingers from around the knife, "and put it away?"

"Of course you'd say something like that," she said, then sat on the bed and began to cry.

He laid the knife on top of the window sill, out of her reach, and put on his jeans, resigned to staying awake the rest of the night. There were other knives in the house, and he couldn't leave until she seemed straight enough not to go out the window after he was gone.

She laid down and appeared to go to sleep, and he sat on the floor, his back against the wall, to wait for dawn. For a while he imagined headlines, *"Drugged girl jumps from window of house she shared with pornographic film stars and drug dealer. Victim said to be linked with Green Beret taking secret classes."*

And he sat and waited for dawn to light the window, thinking of the simplicity and security of the barracks, wishing he was back there, smiling at himself for wishing such a thing. Vietnam was only a couple of months away, he thought, and then he would be able to leave everything behind.

Morning came and she was still asleep, or seemed to be.

"I've got to get back to the base and get some sleep," he said, "are you OK?"

"Sure, I'm OK," she said, sitting up, "but you don't care, do you? You don't fucking care. Nobody does."

"OK," he said, "I'm going," but as he went down the stairs, he heard her behind him on the squeaking stairway, muttering, then shouting at him, "Who cares? Who fucking cares?"

She followed him out the door onto the street where the milk and bread and beer trucks were making their Saturday morning deliveries, and she stayed behind him to the corner, shouting at him, "I don't need you. I'm fine without that shit."

He waited for her at the corner. "Look," he said, "I've got to get some sleep. Go on home, and I'll talk to you later."

"I don't need you," she shouted, "you may think I do, but I don't."

Hanson thought about running, but he'd have felt foolish doing that, and it might even make things worse. He imagined himself running, pursued by a barefoot girl wearing shorts and a man's underwear shirt, and he kept walking as she trailed behind, still shouting. At a busy intersection he thought about racing through the traffic, but worried that she might follow and get hit by a car.

Finally though, he looked behind him, and she was gone. It was a lovely morning, and he began to feel better on the long walk to the bus station. He passed the White House and the smell of roses and flowering trees washed over him. He looked over to see a group of people on a tour of the grounds, dressed in pastels, a winding column of tourists that seemed to sparkle with the silver flashes of their Instamatics.

Outtakes from
Night Dogs
(1990-93)
1

Nine days later, late in the afternoon, he dropped his duffel bag on a condemned wharf near the Embarcadero in San Francisco. He sat at the end of the wharf, at the edge of the continent, as far as he could go, and watched the sun set a thousand miles farther to the west.

He ate beef jerky and a can of peaches, the cars and trucks and busses turning on their lights now on the double-decker bridge high overhead. It had been a long trip. He sat back against the duffel bag, drinking the last of a pint of good Scotch, watching headlights and taillights crossing the sky, and fell asleep listening to the distant rumble and boom of the bridge.

It took four days to find a place to live, a second floor studio apartment above the "Washateria" laundromat in North Berkeley. They required a deposit and first and last month's rent, a lot of money, but it was a sunny apartment and he was tired of riding busses to "For Rent" addresses that had already been taken.

He hadn't realized what a busy neighborhood it was. He'd looked forward to taking a lot of walks, going to bookstores, thinking about what he should do next, but there were too many people, in a hurry, on the sidewalks. All he thought about was hitting people, smashing their faces when they backed into him, or worse, came up on him from behind, pushing through the crowd. By the time he got back to the Washateria he was stooped over, walking like an old man, the taste of pennies under his tongue, his ears ringing with dread.

He forced himself to walk every day, taking breaks on side streets where he could stop and slow his breathing down, hoping he'd get used to it. He lasted less than a week.

Three or four college guys were right behind him in the crowd, laughing, shouting to each other about the touch football game they were coming from. He tried to ignore it, but they kept walking *up* on him, catching imaginary passes, bumping him, until he drove his elbow back, catching one of them in the short ribs and kidneys, dropping him like he'd been shot, flopping and moaning on the sidewalk.

He stood and looked at the others, terror and death in his eyes, and they stepped back, the crowd swirling around them, and Hanson walked away without looking back.

A few days later it was a fat black teenager on a bike. Hanson was walking up one of the side streets he'd found, steep and narrow, leading to a view of the bay. It was quiet, Saturday morning, when the bike topped the hill and raced down, straight at Hanson. The kid was pedaling hard, leaning over the handlebars, screaming, "Move your *Aaassss,* fucker," expecting Hanson to dive for cover.

Hanson sidestepped toward the curb, kicked the bike careening against the side of a brick row-house, and continued up the hill, listening to the kid and the bike flip and skid the rest of the way down the sidewalk. He took a complicated route back to his room, trying not to run or look over his shoulder. He decided not to go out during the day anymore, afraid he'd end up in jail.

It was worse at night–the muggers, looking for easy opportunities, left him alone. But there were drunks, out of money, teenage glue sniffers, panhandlers, psychotics and convicts AWOL from halfway houses.

He was drinking too much during the day, not eating, looking for trouble at night. He woke up in an alley one morning with swollen knuckles and a bloody face. After using tweezers to pick bits of glass and gravel out of his forehead and cheekbone, he made an appointment to see a shrink in a free clinic. Everything was free in California.

It was a big daylight basement that smelled of military floor wax, cigarette smoke and disinfectant. Sunlight filtered through rectangular wire-reinforced windows at the ceiling. The shrink read the questionnaire Hanson filled out, then asked questions.

"I guess it's, obviously, people who challenge me, who make eye contact with me and expect me to look away," Hanson said.

The shrink nodded. Only five or six years older than Hanson, in good shape, he wore jeans, tennis shoes, and a plaid shirt with the sleeves rolled up.

The age of a Captain without much time in grade, Hanson thought. Looks like he plays tennis, or pickup basketball after work with the local black dudes to show he can be one of the guys.

After answering questions for a while, Hanson asked him, "Can you give me a prescription for something, some kind of tranquilizer, so I can go out and walk around?"

"I could do that," he said.

Hanson nodded, trying not to look too anxious.

"But that would be a short term treatment of your *symptoms* –the problem would still be there.

263

"You're not alone, man. I meet a veteran's group–people like you–once a week here where they talk about this shit, get it out in the open and *deal* with it, man. Why don't you come and talk to us?"

Hanson let himself be patronized, nodded, and said he'd think about it.

The shrink told him he was eligible for unemployment payments, and that helped. He started buying cheap vodka in half-pints, forcing himself to walk to the liquor store more often in the hope that he'd drink less, walking drunk to different liquor stores so the clerks wouldn't recognize him as the drunk he was. It didn't work.

He went to a few job interviews, sweating, trying to cover the vodka smell with aftershave, but when they read his answer to "last position held," U. S. ARMY SPECIAL FORCES–VIETNAM, he knew he didn't have a chance.

He went to the Veteran's group, having managed to go all day without a drink. It was like AA, coffee, cookies and lots of cigarette smoke. They were bullshitters, liars and crybabies, saying what they thought the shrink wanted to hear:

"I just wanted to fly helicopters, man. I love to *fly*. Then these lifer motherfuckers send me out on these search and destroy missions. Kill farmers and kids, man. That wasn't *me*. That wasn't what I joined up for."

"People keep asking me, 'When are you gonna put this away,' you know? And I say *never*. How can I forget all that shit?"

A black guy talked about machine-gunning hundreds of charging N.V.A. No one challenged him.

"I was riding the bus," another guy said. He wore a bush hat and fatigue jacket. "And suddenly I was back there and all the other passengers were Viet Cong . . . there was this time over there. It was a firefight off in the distance, and this new guy got scared cause he thought he heard something. So I said, 'Why don't you light a flare, man,' and I was just fucking with him, 'cause if you light a flare, the VC are gonna know your location. But he *did* it, and the VC zeroed in on the flare and killed him. Was it *my* fault? Was it?" he asked the shrink. "I can't sleep, man."

"Don't lose any more sleep over it," Hanson told him. "You weren't even *in* Vietnam."

Hanson shoved his way toward the door. "Fuck you," he said, "fuck all of you."

"We know how you feel, brother," someone said.

"I'm not your fucking *brother*. Get the fuck away from me." They were afraid of him. Except for one.

"You're free to go," said the shrink, "and you're free to come back."

"I'd blow my brains out before I turn into one of these guys," Hanson said.

The guy who wasn't afraid followed him out.

"I know," he said. "They're full of shit. But it's all we've got. I tried everything."

"I'm not doing so good either," Hanson said. "I don't know. Good luck, man," he said, walking away. "You're not like them."

He spent all morning filling out medical histories and psychological questionnaires, and most of the afternoon just waiting in the lobby of the VA hospital, the smell of urine and cigarette smoke mixed with disinfectant. He'd brought a book about mountain men, *Give Your Heart to the Hawks,* but kept looking up from the pages at the crippled and maimed and blind shuffling through the lobby. Most of them, he imagined, had been waiting to die from their wounds since World War Two, abandoned by their families years ago. And who could blame the families, he thought, looking at the pasty, poorly dressed women and children sitting around him. The afternoon sun blazed through the front windows when they called his name, issued him a blue and white plastic ID card, and told him to come back the next day.

Dr. Gantz, a psychiatrist, had an office way off in another wing of the hospital. When he knocked on the heavy oak door, Hanson was a little surprised when it was a woman who said, "Come in, please." She was attractive, in her 40s, with streaked blonde hair, blue eyes, and high cheekbones.

He sat in a straight backed oak chair and watched her look through the brick-red folder with his name on it. Her finger-nails and lipstick were a slightly darker shade of red.

"You are a decorated veteran of a highly disciplined, elite unit, that stresses self-reliance," she said, closing the file. "Why did you come to see me?"

She looked him in the eyes, not letting him look away, as he told her about the anxiety and violence and the drinking.

"Take off your shirt," she said, getting out from behind her desk and locking the door. "Turn around."

She walked up to him and put her hands on his shoulders and ran them down his arms.

"Hold your arms out." She slipped her hands up into his armpits, then slid them down his chest to his waist. She tapped his back with her knuckles.

"Drinking alcohol can only make things worse. Do you not know this?" she said into his ear.

"Yes, ma'am," Hanson said, "that's why I'm here. To get a prescription for something so I won't drink so much."

"How much have you been drinking?" she whispered.

"About. Um. Three half-pints of vodka a day. Sometimes some wine."

"Do you know what that does to your liver?" she demanded, walking back to her desk. "The *damage* that does!

"Take down your trousers."

"Ma'am?"

"Lower your trousers. I want to see if your liver is enlarged."

Hanson unbuttoned and unzipped his jeans and lowered them to his knees.

"Where is your underwear?" she said.

"I stopped wearing them in Vietnam. It was too humid. They caused, you know, a rash."

"How do you expect to stay clean without underwear? *Never* come here filthy like this, without underwear. Do you understand me?"

"Yes, ma'am."

"Come here, then. Put your hands on my desk. Bend over and stand with your legs apart with your hands on my desk."

"Ma'am?"

"I have to check your liver," she said, tearing open a white envelope and taking out a pair of rubber gloves.

"Do you want me to help you or not?" she said. "Come here."

Hanson shuffled over, his pants around his ankles, and put his hands on the desk. "Step back farther," she said, pulling the thin rubber gloves onto her hands, her dark red fingernails looking as though they might cut through. The gloves squeaked and snapped as she pulled them on, releasing the smell of talcum powder. Hanson got a glimpse of a number, six or seven figures, tattooed on the underside of her forearm, when the cuff of her white lab coat slipped down.

"This will only take a moment," she said, squeezing a dollop of clear jelly out of a tube onto the finger of her right hand.

She walked around behind him, put a hand on his shoulder and slowly inserted her finger. "Yes," she said, "I thought so." She pushed farther. "There. The liver is enlarged. Two or three centimeters."

She took her hand off his shoulder and reached down, taking his erection in her gloved hand. "I thought so," she said, removing her finger. "If you have to do this," she said, reaching into the pocket of her lab coat, "you must use one of these." She opened the foil-wrapped condom and slipped it onto him. "Stand up," she said, slipping out of her skirt, keeping the lab coat on.

Afterwards she wrote him a prescription for valium. "Come back in a week," she said. "I have to check you again."

The next week she agreed to double the prescription. He visited her once a week for over a month, and each time she kept her lab coat on. Hanson decided he was a "valium whore," smiling at the idea. It was less demeaning than the Vietnam vets meetings, crying and telling the shrink what he wanted to hear. The valium calmed him down and kept him out of trouble. And he didn't mind the visits. There *was* something erotic about fucking the doctor in her office, while she wore a lab coat.

One week, after getting his unemployment check, Hanson bought a fifth of Irish whiskey and passed out a little after noon, missing his appointment with Dr. Gantz. The police showed up just after dark, and Hanson found himself locked up in an observation room at the VA, "a danger to himself and/or others."

A fat young woman in sweatclothes, a psychiatric aide, saw him first.

"Look," Hanson told her, his head pounding, thinking that he'd give a hundred dollars for a two-dollar half pint of Popov vodka, "I'm sorry I missed my appointment, but I'm not dangerous. Doctor Gantz just, man, she's a little bit crazy."

"'Crazy'," the woman said, STANFORD UNIVERSITY across her sweatshirt. "Is that right? How is she crazy, exactly?"

Hanson looked at the floor, realizing he should shut up.

"Let me tell you something about Dr. Gantz. She could have any job she wanted, ten times the salary she gets in this shithole of a hospital. She's brilliant. Do you know why she stays here? Do you?"

Hanson shook his head.

"She and her whole family were rounded up and sent to Treblinka when she was fourteen. They killed her parents. Then they used her sex until they got tired of her, then *used her* some *more*. For medical experiments. She never takes off her lab coat because of what they did to her. She spent four years there—grew *up* there. When she should have been going to the high school prom. She works in this place, with fuckers like you, because it was American soldiers who liberated her from that camp. To pay them back, somehow. So don't you fuckin' tell me. . . . "

The door was unlocked, and Dr. Gantz came in.

"Thank you, LeeAnn," she said. "I need to talk to Mister Hanson. Would you please excuse us?"

"Did you tell her about our treatment?" she asked him after LeeAnn closed the door.

"I told her you were a little crazy," Hanson said. "Then I decided to shut up."

She laughed. "A little crazy. Wonderful.

"You were good. I enjoyed you. But I've done all I can for you. I can't 'cure' you. Nobody can. Evil is what's troubling you. I know evil when I see it. You think *you* saw evil. What you saw was *nothing,* but you chose to succumb to it. Very well."

She gave him a plastic bag full of valium sample packs.

"Go. If I see you again," she said, "I'll have you committed. You *are* a danger to yourself and others."

She walked out, leaving the door ajar.

Hanson wandered through the halls, looking for the illuminated red EXIT signs that only seemed to lead him to other hallways, past wards of old men, their noses and ears huge, out of proportion to their heads and sunken, toothless mouths. Others on gurneys in the hallway, groaning in their sleep. Hopeless, waiting for death, they looked like pictures he'd seen of concentration camp inmates.

Then it came to him. She worked at the VA hospital because she felt at home there. It reminded her of childhood, of love and sex.

A few days later, Hanson was reading want ads in an out-of-town newspaper someone had left behind in a cafe. They were advertising for police officers in Oregon. He took what money he had left in the bank and bought the VW van, flushed the valium down the toilet, and drove north.

By the time he got to Redding, to Mt. Shasta, he knew it had been a stupid gesture to flush the valium. He couldn't ignore the withdrawal symptoms anymore. He made it to Eugene, willing himself through the tunnel vision, dizziness, the ringing in his ears, panic, making the long drive up the Willamette Valley minute-by-minute.

He pulled off the freeway in Portland, got a bottle of vodka, and managed to find a room for rent, being "nice" to the old lady landlord—sweating, tunnel vision and borderline hallucinations, his ears ringing like doom—making small talk about the weather. She rented him the room, where he laid on the sagging bed for three days and nights, looking at the ceiling, getting off the valium.

He'd been on the street for over three years now.

2

L et's try and get a couple of movers before things get busy,"
Dana said, back in the parking lot.

"How many have you got this month?"

"Three."

"I got two," said Hanson. "No way I'm gonna get ten this month."

"Got's to, young man, got's to," Dana said, "Bendix's gonna get real nervous and a pain in the ass if we don't. You saw the lieutenant looking in at roll call."

"Yeah," Hanson said. "He's got that fuckin' *look* down. Whenever he looks at me I think I'm on my way to Internal Affairs for *something*. Something I forgot about."

"I knew the Lieutenant when we were both patrolmen. He always worried a lot. Sometimes I want to go up to him, put my arm around him and say, 'It's OK, Sir. Smiling isn't a sign of weakness.'"

"We got some *mov*ing vio*la*tions," Hanson sang.

A mover was a "moving traffic violation," running stoplights, speeding, reckless driving, prohibited left turns. Driving with a suspended license was not a mover, even though a person driving while suspended was supposed to go to jail. There was no room in the jail for them. Half the people on the Avenue were suspended. Jaywalking was a mover. Movers brought in money to the city.

Hanson backed the car into a vacant lot just off the Avenue at an intersection where he could see the stoplight from both directions. He pulled the car back far enough so they could be visible to drivers approaching the light only at the last second.

They sat through the cycles of the stoplight, watching first one street, then the other. Each time the light changed from green to yellow, Hanson gripped the gear shift, ready to jerk it from "Park" to "Drive," watching the cars down the street that couldn't make it through the light, but hoping they'd try.

A red VW bug was northbound on the Avenue as the light jumped up from green to yellow. "OK. OK, come on now," Hanson said, leaning forward, hand on the gearshift, "Come on. Blow it. . . . "

The car rolled to a stop.

Hanson and Dana turned their heads to watch eastbound traffic on the cross street, but when the light turned yellow there was nothing in sight. They looked back down the Avenue, their heads moving with each cycle of the light as if they were watching some tremendously slow tennis game.

Five Eighty, radio said.

Five Eighty, the district car answered.

Uh, Five Eighty, we've got a report of a naked man standing in the street at Seventeen and Killingsworth, holding something between his eyes.

What was that last part?

The radio buzzed as the dispatcher keyed his microphone. People were laughing at the communications center, *Uh, Five Eighty. That's what it says on the card here. . . . holding something between his eyes.*

Right. We'll check it out, the car answered. A moment later he added, *and let you know.*

"Hey," Hanson said, looking down the street, "Here it comes. Come *on,* baby."

An old blue Pontiac barreled toward the intersection, rocking on its ruined suspension, the driver looking at the woman sitting next to him.

The light turned yellow.

"Come on, baby. Blow it now. Blow it."

Then the driver glanced out the windshield, saw the police car, his eyes wide. Saw the light. The car shuddered, fishtailed, and ground to a squealing stop in a cloud of blue smoke.

Hanson threw open the door of the patrol car, jumped out and landed in a crouch, threw his arms out, palms down like a baseball umpire, and screamed, "SAFE!"

The driver and the woman in the car were still laughing when the light turned green. The old car rolled by, the two of them waving.

Hanson shook his head and waved back, then got in the car. "You know," he said, "They're paying us eleven dollars an hour for this. I think we look kind of foolish. What do you think?"

"Of course we do. It's part of the job."

Five Fifty . . . we've got a report of an angry brother with a gun at Mississippi and Shaver. Can you go that way?

"Let's take it," Hanson said, putting the car in gear as Dana picked up the mike and said, "Five Sixty Two's close. We can go. You got a description?"

"Fuck a bunch of movers," Hanson said as he bounced over the curb. "We can stop by the graveyard and get some names."

He turned on the overhead lights, made quick eye contact with the drivers of all the cars in the intersection, and ran the red light.

White male, late thirties, five ten. . . .

The car's transmission droned as it slowly picked up speed, the siren yelping.

Five Seventy's got the cover.

273

Copy, Five Seventy . . . . *medium build, with short brown hair. Red plaid Bermuda shorts, and a black T-shirt that says, "HAPPI-NESS IS".* . . *uh* . . .

"Damn Fords," Hanson said, pumping the gas to try and kick it into a lower gear. "What *is* happiness?"

. . . *he's carrying a rifle. On his way to the Techtronics building on Beech Street to kill his brother who works there.*

"What's this guy's name?"

Alvin Weed.

The car lurched forward, coughed, and the speedometer needle moved slowly from 35 toward 40, the overhead lights urgent and absurd.

Hanson cut the lights and siren. "We look like Keystone Cops, you know that? I'm surprised that people take us seriously at *all.*

"Come on honey," he said, hunching back and forth in the seat, "a little more steam."

"Why does he want to shoot his brother?" Dana asked radio.

His wife says he's drunk.

Hanson laughed. "So much for the psychological approach."

"What kind of rifle?"

She says it's a deer rifle. Apparently, the T-shirt says "HAPPINESS IS A LARGE GUT PILE."

Laughing, Hanson flicked on the overhead lights for a second as they passed a slow-moving van, and the startled driver almost steered into them.

"Whoa! Fuck!" Hanson shouted, still laughing.

"How about that lot at Mississippi and Beech," Dana said, "We can see both directions from there."

"Good," Hanson said. "Al. Oh, Al," he sang as the car slowly pushed past fifty, "Pleasedon't. Shootyour. *Brother.* . . . "

When he turned onto Mississippi he began pumping the brakes, slowing down as fast as possible without squealing the tires. A bony man wearing plaid Bermuda shorts and a black "Deer Unlimited" T-shirt was standing on the corner a block away, his back to the patrol car. The only white person in sight, he seemed to be waiting for the light to change from WAIT to WALK. The lever-action deer rifle, a Winchester 94, was tucked casually under his arm.

"I'd guess that's him," Dana said.

"The inner-city sportsman," Hanson said. "My call, OK? Lemme talk to Al."

Little groups of people watched him from doorways and from shadows behind store windows. Two young girls, laughing and talking as they crossed Mississippi, hadn't noticed him. Halfway across the street they froze, then ran back the way they'd come.

"Somebody's gonna blow him out of his socks," Dana said. A lot of people in that part of town carried guns. "So try not to get shot by some armed citizen."

"They can't kill *me*. Not today." Hanson said, watching the man's back and neck, pulling the car to the curb. "I got the *glow* today," he said, unholstering the flat black pistol and thumbing the safety off. He held it close to his leg, low-profile, walking matter-of-factly up behind the man.

"Police officers, Al," he said, bringing his pistol up, "Do *not* move."

"I think you'd better give me that rifle," he said, sliding it easily from under his arm.

Dana was crouched behind the patrol car, his pistol braced on the hood, aimed at Al.

"Now Al. . . . " Hanson said as he backed away, *"No*. Don't turn around. Don't look around. Don't *move* until I tell you to or my partner will shoot you. I'll shoot you too, in the head. OK?"

"Yes sir. I won't cause no trouble."

"OK, Al. Put your hands behind your head and interlace your fingers."

He raised his hands.

"Behind your *head*. Not up in the air.

"Now. Slowly. Turn around."

As Al turned, Hanson looked for bulges in his shirt or shorts that might be a weapon. On the front of the shirt, a red and blue and brown mound of cartoon intestines—steam rising.

"Stop."

Facing Hanson now, a little unsteady, he looked at the sidewalk.

"Got any more guns or knives?" Hanson said. "Tell me the truth now, or I'm gonna be pissed off."

"No sir."

Dana had holstered his pistol and walked up behind Al.

"OK. Just relax and let my partner handcuff you then," and Dana brought Al's arms down and snapped on the cuffs.

"Look at me, Al," Hanson said.

He looked up, eyes not quite focused, exhausted. The skin on his face was translucent with fatigue. He smelled of alcohol and the vomit that smeared his T-shirt and Bermuda shorts.

"How long have you been drinking?"

"What day is it?" he asked.

"Wednesday."

"Three days?"

They walked him over to the patrol car and Hanson holstered his pistol. He worked the action of the rifle and patted Al down. Three boys on bikes watched from the sidewalk.

"Not loaded."

"OK, Al," Hanson said, "Just stay where you are until we check on some things."

"Yes sir. Whatever you say, sir," he said, and assumed a rigid position of "attention," staring sternly over the hood of the car.

"At ease."

"Yes sir," Al said, taking a wider stance. Hanson read the serial number of the rifle to Dana before locking it in the trunk. Dana ran a radio check on Al and the rifle.

While they waited with the radio chattering, Al studied the inside of the police car. "One of the old Fords, huh?" he said.

"Yeah, the Chevy's in the shop. Al," Hanson said, "do you understand that you almost got shot just now?"

"Yes sir," he said, "No excuse sir."

One of the boys laughed. "What kinda fool walking around with an unloaded gun? Next time one of the brothers gonna shoot his ass."

"Come on guys," Hanson told them, "take off, OK?"

"Is it against the law to be on the sidewalk?"

"Get outta here," Dana said.

They looked at him for a moment, then pedaled off, whooping and doing wheelies.

"Al, what did you think you were going to do with that unloaded rifle?"

He shrugged and looked down at the street.

"Carrying a gun around here, even if it's unloaded–especially if it's unloaded, is gonna get you shot."

"Yes sir. I'll remember to load it."

Radio told them that Al didn't have any outstanding warrants. There was no record of the rifle being stolen.

Dana thumbed through the little yellow city code manual and shook his head. "If nobody wants to sign a complaint, he hasn't broken any city or state laws."

They probably could have arrested him under some federal gun-control law, but the paperwork would keep them off the street for the rest of the afternoon, and the agents over at ATF would piss and moan about the extra work. They were only interested in big busts, machine guns and pipe bombs.

"Well, Al," Hanson said as Dana took off the handcuffs, "You're free to go, but I'm going to have to take the rifle for safe-keeping. . . . "

"My *Winchester*? Officer, I've had that rifle for—"

"Al," Hanson said, holding up his left hand to interrupt him, "we've been nice guys, haven't we? We didn't shoot you or arrest you or anything, right?"

"Yeah, but. . . . "

"I'm gonna give you a receipt for the rifle and you can pick it up at the police property room in three days. I have to follow orders. You understand that, don't you?"

"Yes sir. Sorry."

"Three days. The police station property room downtown. Any questions?"

"How do you like those new Chevys?" he asked. "I hear they're pretty fast."

"I meant . . . fast enough for driving in town. Good low-end torque. We gotta get going now. Do me a favor and don't be carrying a gun around no more, OK? And *don't* go bother your brother. Can I trust you not to do that?"

"You can count on me, Officer," he said, holding out his hand, "it's been a real pleasure. You know, I always wanted to be a police officer myself."

"Well," Hanson said, shaking his hand, "Thanks. Take care now."

"Right, Officer Hanson. And listen," he said, lowering his voice, "if you ever need any help on anything, don't hesitate to call."

"OK. Thanks. Gotta go."

His hand on the door handle, Hanson watched Al jaywalk into the street.

"Hey, Al," Hanson shouted, "Would you please come here a minute?"

Al walked back, smiling.

"Don't jaywalk in front of a *police* car. It looks like you don't have any respect for us. Makes us look bad, you know?"

"Sorry, officer."

"I'm gonna have to give you a citation for jaywalking."

"Right. I deserve it."

"I need to see that ID again."

As Hanson wrote the ticket, Al asked, "I was wondering, uh, how much will it cost?"

"Twenty-two dollars," Hanson said, still writing. He flipped the cover of the citation book open to find a court date. "Is that a major problem?"

"I can get it, sir."

"Where you working now? Al?"

"I was working at Techtronics, but I got, I had a little trouble."

Hanson looked up at him, then tore the citation out and crumpled it up. "I think you've learned your lesson. But don't go to Techtronics, OK? If you do it'll make me look real bad, like I didn't take care of the problem."

"You have my word, sir."

"OK, Al. Have a nice day. And remember," Hanson said, pointing toward the corner, "Cross at the green and not in between."

Al smiled, waved, and tripped on the curb.

"That was a mover you tore up," Dana said as they drove off.

"Fuck the lieutenant. I didn't want to deal with Al anymore, go to court, nothing. I was starting to forget which one of us was the crazy person."

Dana told radio they'd be out at the property room, then took out a pen, and folded his newspaper to the want ads, "Investment Property."

Hanson took the new memorial bridge and got on the freeway.

"That was awful easy," Dana said. "Too easy. You know that, don't you, my man? That was probably *not* the way to approach a man with a gun on his way to kill his brother."

"It's *all* easy," Hanson said, grinning. "Adventures in law enforcement. I saw you over there ready to blow old Al away. You wouldn't let Al shoot me. Besides, how would you do it 'by the book?' You got a crazy guy with a rifle on a crowded street. What are you gonna do? Call the whole precinct in to cordon off the area? Wait an hour for the fucking SWAT team?"

"Angle park the patrol vehicle," he went on, assuming the tone of an academy instructor, "in order to place the bulk of the engine between you and the armed suspect. Utilizing the PA system, and speaking in a command voice, inform the suspect that he is to drop his weapon and walk–slowly–backwards.

"Yeah," Hanson said, in his own voice, "that's the stuff. Oh boy. But what if the suspect doesn't want to *do* that? What if he thinks you're the voice of the devil that's been after him, and starts shooting people? Then, when it's all over, some lieutenant is gonna say you should have done something *else*. Fuck it. What we did worked. Yes, yes," he said, "look at that blue sky."

"Who am I gonna get for a partner if you get blown away?" Dana said.

"How about Duncan? He's got that college degree in criminal justice. I'll bet he's read a chapter in a book about how to deal with a guy like Al."

"Forget I mentioned it."

"Very well, your honor. If you have any more questions, though, 'Don't. Hesitate. To call.'"

After dropping the rifle off at the property room they hit the street without notifying radio, and took a detour through an old, predominately black cemetery. It was weed-choked, tombstones sagging in the clay and sand soil, Johnson grass and standing water where the earth had settled above the coffins. The patrol car bounced and bottomed out as they drove the dirt road, a few of the graves decorated with mayonnaise jars full of stagnant water and dead flowers, a few dried up wreathes, their ribbons faded by the sun and rain.

They stopped at a fresh grave and got out of the car. Little white wildflowers, tiny morning glories, threaded through the grass among the tombstones, and Hanson took care not to step on any of them. The name painted on the cheap new concrete was "Frederic Eli Walker."

"That's Fast Fred," Dana said. "It's the name on his mug-shot."

"I didn't know he was dead."

"I thought the old fucker was too tough to die."

"We *almost* shot him that time when he was drunk on his porch with his shotgun."

"You were lucky that time, Fred," Hanson said, shaking his finger at the grave.

Dana smiled. "Remember what he told the judge after he threatened to charge him with contempt?"

"'What you all gonna do when I'm dead and you can't *fuck* with me no more? Dig up my grave and sentence me to hell?'"

281

"We won't do that, but you do need a couple of citations, Fred. What do you think? Speeding and . . . disobey traffic light."

"Have a nice day, Fred."

They found one more fresh grave before notifying radio and heading back to the district, a seventeen year old kid who was killed trying to elude the police in a stolen car two weeks before.

"Another speeding ticket," Hanson said.

They'd give the information to Debbie Deets, the cop groupie famous for her blowjobs who worked in records. She could run their names in NCIC, get their DOB, address and car registration. Then they could complete the citation and turn it in. The city would mail court notices, then issue arrest warrants, and it would be months, maybe years, before they'd find out the defendant was dead.

They settled a family fight and radio sent them to take a report on obscene phone calls.

"He's been doing it for months," the woman said, "months. I feel like I've gotten to know him, but my husband told me I should call the police."

"Calling us was the best thing to do," Dana said.

"He knows when I'm home and when I'm not. He must watch me all the time."

She was white and heavyset, in her forties, and wore her hair in a pair of ponytails, like handles, one on each side of her head. She took Dana and Hanson into the kitchen that was dominated by a sofa-size reproduction of the Last Supper hung over the kitchen table. A plastic replica of a small loaf of bread sat between the painstakingly hand-painted salt and pepper shakers, the two stone tablets on which the ten commandments were inscribed, five on the salt and five on the pepper. The plastic bread loaf had a hinged top and was filled with cards bearing Bible verses, THE BREAD OF LIFE painted in the side of the brown plastic.

"I read the Bible to him, New Testament. I keep it right by the phone, open to where I left off the last time he called. I started with St. Matthew, and we're halfway through Corinthians now," she said, holding the bible up. "Sometimes he'll go on for an hour or more."

It was Dana's call, and he began filling out the crime report at the table. Hanson stood back against the refrigerator, half watching the small black and white TV on the counter next to the sink, a quiz show.

"What sort of things does he say?" Dana asked her.

"Well, I hate to say."

"I understand, but if I'm going to help you here, I have to put his exact words into my report."

"It's things he says he wants. To do to me."

"Sexual acts?"

She looked out the window. "Indecent acts. Perversions. Using bodily parts for things I never even knew about, thought about, until he started calling."

Hanson grinned at Dana and wiggled his tongue.

"You know," Dana said, "maybe I can just say he suggested sexual acts, using graphic language. . . . "

"Graphic?"

"Very specific. Dirty language."

"The most graphic I ever heard. He started off telling me to, well," she said, lowering her voice, "touch myself. If you have to know, I can tell you his exact words. 'Wouldn't you like to spread your legs. . . . '"

She scooted her chair closer to Dana, and Hanson couldn't hear her over the TV and the rumbling refrigerator.

There was a pause after a commercial and Hanson stared hard at the silent TV.

" . . . his tongue. 'Then I'll roll you over. . . . ' "

"Yes, Ma'am," Dana said, "I think that's all I need for now. The best thing to do, next time he calls, is just hang up right away. Don't say anything to him. He'll get bored and start calling somebody else."

"You think that will make him stop?"

"Yes, Ma'am. Whoops," he said, pulling the chattering packset from his belt as if he'd just gotten a call. "Right," speaking into the packset without pressing the 'transmit' button. "Right away," he said, getting up.

"We've got an emergency," he told Hanson.

"An emergency? What is it?"

Dana smiled grimly at him and nodded. "A shooting. Two shootings."

"Wow. We better get going."

"Remember," Dana told the woman as he gathered up his paperwork, "hang up on him the next time he calls."

"You think he'll leave me alone then?"

"See if it doesn't work," he said over his shoulder as he and Hanson headed for the door.

"I think I'll stay with the Bible. That's what he needs. If he starts calling someone else he'll just get worse."

Dana and Hanson ran to the car, turned on the overhead lights, and drove off laughing.

"Could you hear what she told me?" Dana said.

"I heard just enough."

"Damn. That old biscuit was getting me a little . . . worked up."

"More scriptures, oohhh. Yes! *Read* it to me momma," Hanson said. " 'Neither fornicators, nor adulterers, nor the effeminate, nor abusers of *themselves* will inherit the Kingdom of God.' Ohhh baby."

"What's that?"

"Somewhere in Corinthians."

"I didn't know you had a religious background."

"I learned it in the Army. The only book you could read in basic training was the Bible. I carried it around and read it to keep from going nuts."

They passed a burned-out house, plywood over the windows pale against the charred siding where plaster lath showed through in spots like ribs.

"Remember me telling you about that black guy I worked with in Vietnam? The one we called 'Doc?'"

"I remember you mentioned him."

"He killed a guy stateside that he knew was flashing an unloaded pistol. On a thirty day leave before his second tour. He knew it was unloaded. Killed him just for fun."

"I don't know about you sometimes, my son," Dana said. "No wonder people look at you funny sometimes."

"He wasn't any kind of nice guy, but you could sure depend on him."

A black cat, hunting in the tall grass of a vacant lot, watched them drive past.

Hanson smiled. Anyone looking at his eyes would have thought he was recalling a happy childhood.

"Still," Dana said, "I don't think it was a good idea to remind Al to load his rifle. Good for Al maybe, but not for the rest of the world."

"Doc said they couldn't *prove* he knew it was unloaded. 'And *besides*,' he'd say, 'I'm a motherfuckin' *war* hero, on my way back to fight the bad ole Communists some more.'"

It was dusk. Nighthawks swooped like shadows above the children playing the streets. *"Po*-lice. *Po*-lice," they called as the patrol car rolled through the neighborhood. The police were as much a part of their lives as breakfast and bedtime. *"Po*-lice," they called, their voices like the cooing of doves.

Five Sixty Two

Dana picked up the mike, "Five Six Two."

Uh, Five Sixty Two, we've got a report of a man with a gun...

"Well, damn," Hanson said, "we're never gonna get to supper."

3

Hanson had agreed to work the day for the Vice Division, arresting prostitutes. He'd done it once before, when he was a rookie, and he'd almost gotten shot.

Vice gave him twenty dollars out of their petty cash fund so he could pay for drinks in bars. But like most of the uniformed guys who worked a day for Vice, he planned to just arrest them on the street. All he had to do was pull alongside the curb when he saw a prostitute and talk to her until they agreed on "an act and a price," and then tell her she was under arrest. There was usually time to take the first prostitute back to the station and do the paperwork on her, then make one more pass down the Avenue for another arrest. After that, word would be out on the street, his cover would be blown, and no one else would talk to him. Then he'd have the rest of the day and night off, with Vice's twenty bucks to spend however he wanted to.

Hanson was nervous as he drove the old unmarked Dodge across the downtown bridge towards North precinct. Even though he was a cop, he was embarrassed about picking up whores. And he knew they'd ask him, "Are you a cop?" They always asked that, and he wasn't a good liar. So he tried to construct an identity where his nervousness would seem normal.

Most of the whores worked the Avenue, and the blocks either side of it, at the border of North Precinct and East Precinct. They stood on the corners and walked the blocks, sometimes in groups of two or three, striking poses and laughing. It was a prostitute supermarket. Tricks, almost all of them white men, cruised the blocks in their family cars on their lunch hours. After dark, things got more tense on the Avenue. The whores moved off the street and into the bars, and their pimps kept a closer eye on them. Pimps mostly stayed out of sight during the afternoon, not wanting to scare the lunch crowd away.

It was a nice day, cooler than it had been, almost like spring, as Hanson made his first pass through the blocks. The tricks were as obvious as the whores, driving everything from Mercedes to broken down pickup trucks, driving slow. Some of them just liked to talk to the whores, some enjoyed insulting them, calling them whores and bitches and sluts, then driving off, laughing.

The whores had a hard life. They had to get into cars with men who, for the most part, despised them—who might shoot them or beat them or take them somewhere and torture them to death. Men whose penises they had to put in their mouths. They had to turn a certain number of tricks every day to keep their pimp from beating them. Who could blame them for trying to stay high on drugs to soften the edge of their lives? Most of them lived in rent-by-the-week motel rooms with their pimps and their babies. Filthy rooms littered with fast food containers, potato chips, wine bottles and cigarette butts, dirty diapers and tampons, where the TV was always on and the curtains always closed and most of the people in the room were so strung out they didn't know if it was night or day. The air would be stale and humid with sweat and cigarette smoke. Sometimes they were runaways, from Seattle or Tacoma or small towns in the eastern part of the state. White girls with acne who might have been cute but were going flabby and pale on drugs. Lost forever. There was no coming back from the drugs and pimps and twenty dollar blowjobs in parked cars.

What kind of dreams did they have when they came to the city, and where did they go when they got too old to turn tricks?

Hanson cruised the block, and the whores turned to pout at him, or blow kisses or smile and rub their crotches. "Hey," they called out to him, "Cutie pie. Come on over here." Hanson blushed and smiled and drove on. He knew half the prostitutes from work. He'd talked to them and arrested a couple of them, but out of uniform they didn't recognize him. He was just another trick in his jeans and tennis shoes and knit shirt. He *did* look different in the uniform and steel-toed boots, with the nightstick and pistol, handcuffs and mace, the extra clips of bullets and the crackle and static of the packset. In the uniform he was ready for combat. That was the message of the uniform. He would talk to you and even let you yell at him once or twice, but you didn't touch him. If you touched him, everything changed. If you touched him you would be handcuffed and taken to jail. If you resisted you would be beaten up until you stopped resisting and *then* taken to jail.

Whenever Hanson talked to someone on the street, wearing the uniform, that was the rule. If you touched him you went to jail. Like a stripper in a bar. You could leer at her and yell things at her as much as you wanted, but if you touched her the show was over and the bouncer would be on you.

He took a right turn, past a bus stop where an old black couple sat, past a kid on a tricycle and a burned-out house. He decided to pretend he'd gone back to college while his wife supported him. He'd never picked up a prostitute before and he was nervous and felt guilty, but he'd been thinking about it for months. He was majoring in English and wanted to get a teacher's certificate.

Up the street a black whore in a purple miniskirt with a sleeveless satin blouse saw him. She was pretty. Dark complexion and curly black hair with the shine of Miracle Dynel. She flipped up the bottom of her skirt, then put both fists on her hips and watched him pull to the curb.

Hanson had put his gun and badge and packset and handcuffs up under the seat next to the driver's door. He decided it was time to go ahead and try to make the first arrest. It was a good spot. There weren't any other people standing around to cause trouble if she decided to resist arrest.

When he pulled to the curb she walked up to the car and looked in the passenger window. A scar, so fine and thin that it could have been made by a surgeon, ran from her forehead, across her eyelid, and faded out on her cheek. The eyelid drooped slightly lower than the other. Her earlobe was ragged where more than one earring had been torn from it, more than once. Still, she was a handsome woman. She looked at him, the scarred eyelid almost sleepy-looking but the eyes themselves fierce as a hawk's.

"What you doing down *here,* honey? she said. "You lost? You take the wrong ramp off the freeway?"

Hanson blushed. "I was, uh, just kind of looking around," he said. She was younger than he was.

"Is that right?" she said. "What is it you lookin' for?"

"Well, you know. . . . " Hanson said.

"You lookin' for a lady? That what you want?"

"Yes Ma'am," Hanson said.

"Yes *Ma'am?"* she said, smiling, "Now I *like* that," she said, opening the door of the car and getting in. "You kind of cute, too."

She looked around the car. "Uh huh," she said to herself. Her black arms were muscular, their fine color blemished by scars on the inside of her forearms. Her hands were graceful, silver rings on the long fingers. When she put her left arm on the back of the seat, glancing down into the back of the car, the muscles in her shoulder and at the curve of her breast bunched and flowed against the satin strap of her blouse. She leaned back, exposing a tuft of black hair in her armpit. The car smelled of her sweat and perfume and cigarette smoke in her hair.

She looked at Hanson, then opened the glove box and looked through it. She looked him up and down. "Are you a cop?" she said.

"What?" Hanson said. "No." He laughed nervously. "I'm, well. I had a stupid job, but I'm going back to school. If I had to say what I really am, I'd say that I was a poet. I don't make any money from it but it's what I value most."

She arched her eyebrows. "A *poet?* You the first one of those I've run into. You sure you like *ladies?*"

"Oh yeah," Hanson said. "I'm just. Kind of nervous."

"Lemme check you out then, see you don't have guns and handcuffs and shit, you know?" she said, patting his shirt down to his waist. She ran her hand down between his legs and paused there. "Uh huh. What did you have in mind?"

"Um," Hanson said.

"You want a date?" She closed her hand around his penis. "Looks to me like you want a date."

"Uh huh," Hanson said. "I've just never done this before."

"That's all right, honey. It's *easy*. You *sure* you not a cop?" she said.

"Uh huh."

"Show me your Willie then."

"What?"

"Show me your *dick*. Your cock, you know? Your pee-nis, you understand? I know a cop can't do that. If you *not* a cop, you can. Come one, honey. I'm gonna see it *any*way, and I gotta be sure."

Hanson unzipped his pants and showed her.

She smiled. "Well, look here. He's wide awake now. What you want to do?"

"Well," Hanson said, blushing again, trying to get himself back into his pants, "maybe just a regular, uh, fuck?"

"Honey," she said, putting her hand on the inside of Hanson's thigh, "that's awful hard to do in the front seat of a car. Why don't we just go somewhere and I'll give you a nice French, you know, a blowjob."

"OK," Hanson said. "How much is that?"

"Twenty dollars," she said. "But you can *tip* me if you want to."

That was it. To make an arrest, all Hanson needed was for her to agree to an act and a price.

"What's your name?" he asked her.

"Yolanda, honey."

"Yolanda," he said, "I'm afraid I lied. I *am* a cop and you're under arrest."

She looked at him, then looked at the door. "Don't do it," Hanson said. "If I have to fight you we'll both just get our clothes messed up." He grabbed her arm with one hand and took her purse with the other. He stuffed the purse between himself and the door and got his handcuffs.

"I'm sorry," he said, "but I have to handcuff you."

"Oh man," she said, "How come you *lie* to me like that?"

"Come on, Yolanda. Put your wrists behind your back and turn 'em around this way."

She slid toward the door and Hanson tightened his grip on her arm. "Don't piss me *off*," he said, his voice harder.

She stopped and looked at him. "I know you," she said, "you're a cop."

292

"Correct."

"No," she said. "I *know* you. I saw you on the street lots of times. I just didn't recognize you without a uniform. Shit."

"Gimme your wrists," Hanson said, and she turned so he could put the handcuffs on. The insides of her wrists were crosshatched with fine ash-gray scars.

"Come on," she said, "don't arrest me. If I get arrested again, I'm gonna have to do some *jail* time. Thirty days. With all those bitches and whores and ugly old bull dyke guards. Please?"

"Yolanda, you know I can't un-arrest you," he said, reaching over to buckle her in with the seat belt. He could feel her breath on the back of his neck. It smelled like marijuana smoke and sweet wine.

He straightened up as she glared at him. He pulled her purse out. "You got any weapons in here?" he said.

"No I don't have any 'weapons.'"

Hanson looked in the purse and pulled out a steak knife with a mean looking serrated blade. The word SIZZLER was burned into the wooden handle. He looked at her.

"Well," she said, "I gotta have *something* to, you know, defend myself with."

Hanson looked at her, the scar across her eye, the ragged earlobe, and tossed the knife out the window of the car. He looked through the rest of the junk in her purse, makeup, a comb, a coupon for free French fries with the purchase of a Big Mac, a creased photograph of a four year old girl, her hair braided in cornrows, cigarettes, gum. He unzipped a side compartment and found two balloons of heroin. Two green rubber balls like lopsided marbles. Dealers packaged it that way so they could carry it in their mouths when they were on the street, and swallow it if the cops grabbed them. No evidence, no arrest. They could vomit it back up later and sell it.

Hanson zipped it back up and put the purse on the seat. The heroin possession was a felony. He got out the packset and told radio that he had a woman prisoner and gave his location.

Copy jackpot with an adult female at . . . three fourteen P.M., radio said. You always give the time and location when you take a woman to jail, in case she claims that you stopped and molested her on the way.

They drove on in silence for a while, past the littered yards and sagging porches where black men sat looking at nothing, drinking from paper bags. Past a group of teenaged boys on a corner passing a bottle around. They glared at him as he drove by. Past kids playing in vacant lots, too young to know yet that they were doomed. At a stoplight he looked way up the street at a kid in his late teens, muscular, his skin very dark, jogging down the side of the street.

It was Aaron Allen, the first time Hanson had seen him since he'd been arrested for robbery and assault, and his Cadillac had been impounded. He had weights buckled to his ankles and was carrying cast iron dumbbells in his hands. Hanson sat through the light cycle watching the kid come. The sun was bright and Aaron's chest gleamed with sweat as he rain, pumping the weights, past the cars lining the street, shiny new dope deal cars, dirty old Chevys and Pintos, abandoned and stripped junk cars with no tires and broken windows where derelicts slept. He kept running past the trash and clutter washed up against the curb, past the living dead clustered outside the liquor stores. He ran through the intersection and looked at Hanson's white face with pure hate, then looked back up the street and kept running.

The light changed again and Hanson drove on, Aaron almost like something he'd imagined. The Spirit of *Will* in the ghetto. Maybe hate was the only thing that could save him from going under like everyone else. Probably it would only get him thrown in jail and, finally, killed. That was a way of escaping.

He took the on-ramp to the freeway, curving above a vacant lot that people used as a dump, mattresses and tires and old TV sets half-hidden in the tall brown grass.

"Don't you ever get tired of taking people to jail?" Yolanda asked him.

"Sometimes," he said. "Sometimes I *like* it though. A lot of times people *deserve* to go to jail."

"You think *I* deserve to go to jail?" she asked him.

"You broke the law," he said.

She laughed. "I don't know whose law it is, but it isn't anything *I* voted for."

Hanson parked in front of Central Precinct, downtown, where the vice office was. He walked Yolanda across the sidewalk and through the big front doors as shoppers and businessmen watched her strut in her high heels, her head high.

Just as Hanson punched the UP button on an elevator, the doors on another one opened and Fox stepped out. "Yo*lan*da," Fox said, his hands full of computer printouts, "Still peddling your ass on the Avenue?"

"You and your *momma* are whores," Yolanda said.

"And you're a fuckin' junkie animal," Fox said, walking toward her. She pursed her lips as if she were going to spit on him and Hanson put his arm around her and turned her away. "John," Hanson said, "why don't you just go on ahead and have a nice day and let me take my prisoner upstairs? OK?"

Just then the doors on the other elevator opened. "Come on," Hanson said, walking her inside. He turned and looked at Fox until the doors closed.

Hanson made one more arrest, an 18 year old with a cast on one arm that she had jammed in the sleeve of the short-waisted leather jacket that matched her leather miniskirt. Because of the cast he had to handcuff her hands in front of her and run the seatbelt through the cuffs.

She was up from San Francisco and angry, claiming that Hanson had "entrapped" her. In California, she said, the cops couldn't offer money until the prostitute named both an act and a price. "This isn't California," Hanson told her, "The law's different here."

"If I get arrested fair," she said, "that's one thing. But this ain't fair." She stared silently through the windshield as they drove downtown, and Hanson felt bad because she really *thought* that he had been unfair.

"How'd you break your arm?"

"I fell *down,"* she said, glaring out the windshield.

"OK, fine," Hanson said. "The law is *different* up here."

"Uh huh," she said, "that's what you told me," still looking straight ahead. "The law."

After he had booked her into vice division, Hanson took one more half-hearted swing through the district, hoping that his cover *was* blown so he could quit for the day. Two arrests was all they really expected, so he wasn't going to try very hard for a third. He was tired of the game and couldn't help feeling a little guilty even though he told himself that it was stupid to feel that way. He was just doing his job.

At a stoplight he remembered the two balloons of heroin in his pocket. He'd taken them out of Yolanda's purse in the elevator. He opened the door a crack, and dropped them on the street.